Geog

DAVID FLINT

CW00701880

TEACHER
TIMESAVERS

Published by Scholastic Publications Ltd,
Villiers House,
Clarendon Avenue,
Leamington Spa,
Warwickshire CV32 5PR

© 1993 Scholastic Publications Ltd

Author David Flint
Editor Jo Saxelby
Series designer Joy White
Designers Micky Pledge and Keith Martin
Illustrations Cathy Hughes and The Drawing Room
Cover illustration Frances Lloyd
Cover photograph Martyn Chillmaid

Designed using Aldus Pagemaker
Processed by Pages Bureau, Leamington Spa
Artwork by Steve Williams Design, Leicester
Printed in Great Britain by Clays Ltd, St Ives plc

British Library Cataloguing-in-Publication Data
A catalogue record for this book is
available from the British Library.

ISBN 0-590-53048-8

All rights reserved. This book is sold subject to the condition that it shall not, by way of trade or otherwise, be lent, hired out or otherwise circulated without the publisher's prior consent in any form of binding or cover other than that in which it is published and without a similar condition, including this condition, being imposed upon the subsequent purchaser.

No part of this publication may be reproduced, stored in a retrieval system, or transmitted, in any form or by any means, electronic, mechanical, photocopying, recording or otherwise, without the prior permission of the publisher. This book remains copyright, although permission is granted to copy pages 11 to 144 for classroom distribution and use only in the school which has purchased the book.

Contents

Geography

Introduction

This book aims to provide resources which will enable teachers to introduce children of 5 to 11 years to key geographical skills and themes. The tasks provide opportunities for children to both apply and test their knowledge of geographical ideas and skills.

The chart on page 10 shows the links between each activity and the National Curriculum geography attainment targets. The development of map skills is covered in detail in the Mapwork section but, because of its underlying importance, recurs in all the other sections of the book.

The activities may also provide useful evidence of individual pupil attainment, although they should not be the only type of assessment. They may also be used to diagnose individual children's difficulties, particularly in relation to aspects such as mapwork or understanding the physical environment.

Using the photocopiable sheets

These sheets should form part of an integrated scheme of work and should reinforce aspects of the subject introduced elsewhere. They can, however, be used to serve a dual function; as reinforcement activities for some children and enhancement activities for others. Some preliminary discussion will be necessary before giving these sheets to the children, but the amount of initial explanation is left to your professional judgement. While children can work individually on these activities, preliminary and/ or follow-up group discussion is valuable.

Please read the following notes before handing out the activity sheets and ensure that they form part of a coherent whole within the theme or topic.

Within each section, the sheets are arranged in ascending order of ability level, but do not relate to specific statements of attainment at that level.
❏ denotes ideas for extension activities.

Mapwork

Where? (Level 1) This activity introduces locational language. Maps essentially show where things are located, so the right vocabulary is important.
❏ Play a form of 'Simon says' with the children standing in, on, beside or behind objects.

Where things are (Level 1)
❏ Encourage the children to add items to other pictures, in each case emphasising the words which describe the location of the items they have added.

Symbols (Level 1) Explain that maps use symbols to represent things. Let the children devise their own.

Buildings as symbols (Level 2)
❏ Challenge the children to design and make signs to be placed at strategic points around the school.

Plans (Level 2) A vital element of all maps is their use of the plan view. This activity encourages children to visualise objects as they would appear from above.
❏ Ask the children to draw plan views of other objects such as furniture, toys, food or cutlery.

Toy plans (Level 2)
❏ Ask the children to draw other layouts of toys in plan view and then as seen from ground level.

The neighbourhood (Level 2) First discuss the relationship between the picture and the plan, highlighting what the features look like.

Left and right (Level 2) Ask the children to first identify their own left and right arms and legs.

In the maze (Level 2)
❏ Challenge the children to design their own mazes and find routes through each other's, counting the number of left and right turns.

Joanne's bedroom (Level 2) This activity shows how maps are useful in depicting routes.
❏ Draw other routes around Joanne's bedroom.

Routes around school (Level 2)
❏ Use other colours to draw routes between classrooms 3, 4 and 5 to other areas of the school.

Routes through town (Level 2) Discuss what the sheet shows to ensure that children see this as a plan of an area. Ask them to name the key features.

Keys on maps and plans (Level 2) Each symbol should bear a relationship to the fruit or vegetable being located, so pictures of these would be useful.
❏ Make comparisons between the different symbols devised and vote to establish the 'best' symbol.

Directions (Level 2) Introduce the main points of the compass and the convention that north is usually at the top of the page.

Following directions (Level 3) This sheet begins the process of combining two or more of the elements of map reading; in this case, route planning and directions. Revise the points of the compass.

On the shelf (Level 3) Introduce simple letter-number grids using a labelled classroom bookcase. Put items in the correct compartment on each shelf.

Finding things (Level 3)
❏ Children can draw and label their own grids and play battleships or other location games. Stress the importance of letter first and number second.

The United Kingdom (Level 3)
❏ Challenge the children to work out, using an atlas, how many counties they would visit on a motor tour from London to Edinburgh and then on to Cardiff.

Compass points (Level 4) Display a compass-rose in the classroom or painted on the playground.

Grids and symbols (Level 4) Make sure that the children understand that the sea will be to the east and the land to the west of the map.

Four-figure grid references (Level 4) This activity combines ideas about symbols and grids. Stress that the reference refers to the bottom left-hand corner of the square.

❑ Ask the children to devise symbols for other features (post office, pylon, shop, cliff) and add these to the map and then give their grid references.

Distances (Level 4) The children should use the straight edge of a piece of paper for measuring and then place this against a ruler to calculate the distances.

Aeroplane travel (Level 4)
❑ Ask the children to measure the straight-line distances between other possible pairs of cities shown on the map.

Routes to school (Level 4)
❑ Add other children's homes to the map, then describe their routes to or from school.

Europe (Level 4) This task and the following one will need reference to atlases.
❑ Additionally, the children could name a country which has no coastline, three countries with a coastline on the Baltic Sea and two countries with a coastline on the Adriatic Sea.

Towns and countries in Europe (Level 4)
❑ Identify these locations: 40°N 5°W; 60°N 10°E; 60°N 15°E; 40°N 23°E.

Six-figure grid references (Level 5) Some children may need help distinguishing between main grid lines (in bold) and the subdivisions of these into tenths. Stress that they must give the numbers along the base of the map first.

Modelling contours (Level 5) This activity forms an important stepping-stone to understanding how contours show the height and shape of the land.

Up and down (Level 5) Use this page as a follow-up to the previous activity.

A contour map (Level 5) Check that the children understand that the figures given on each contour are the height of the land in metres above sea level and that they see in which direction the land is rising.

Holiday snaps (Level 5) This assessment activity will show the extent to which contours are understood.

Places to live

Lucy's house (Level 1) Stress that homes vary greatly. Children living in blocks of flats may need more help initially to decide how to show their homes.

Building materials (Level 1) Provide examples of bricks, tiles, slates, small sheets of glass and plastic pipes and gutters for a preliminary discussion.
❑ Let the children draw pictures of their own houses, labelled to show what each part is made from.

Going shopping (Level 2) As a preliminary activity, let the children unpack a shopping bag and put the items under shop headings.
❑ Add more items to be allocated to the various shops. Remember some items, such as crisps, may be bought in more than one type of shop.

Different homes (Level 2)
❑ Carry out a survey around school. How many of each different type of home can be seen?

Under our feet (Level 3)
❑ Survey a street near school and list all the activities going on above the ground.

People on the move (Level 3) Before attempting this activity, encourage the children to discuss the differences between 'push' factors (usually negative: noise, crime, pollution and traffic jams) and 'pull' factors (usually positive: fresh air, people with similar interests, services geared to entertainment).

Different types of towns (Level 3) Look at aerial photographs or postcards and discuss the various types of towns. Emphasise key features – factories or beaches – which characterise each type of town.

City centre (Level 3) Discuss different types of land use before presenting this activity. The aim is to highlight the variety of land uses found in a city centre and how they differ from, say, a suburb.
❑ Survey land use in a street near school. Ask the children to record their findings using the same colour key. What are the differences between this street and the city centre on the activity page?

Different land uses (Level 4) Children need to understand the importance of plan view and land use maps before attempting this activity.
❑ Find clues to changes in the locality, such as street names and dates on buildings.

The changing street (Level 4)
❑ Discuss what changes could be made locally to improve the quality of the environment.

Developing the area (Level 5) Discuss the special requirements of each development. For example, car parks need a large site and should be situated on the edge of a shopping area, a housing estate also needs a large site but near open space, a superstore needs to be near a motorway, while an industrial estate can use derelict land.

Work

People who help us (Level 1)
❑ Describe the work of other 'people who help us'.

Problems of quarrying (Level 2) Children need to understand that there are different types of work, some of which can create problems for local people.
❑ Discuss local problems, such as traffic congestion. How might these problems be resolved?

Opencast coal-mining (Level 2) Discuss what is happening in the scene and why coal is important.

Work dangers (Level 3)
❑ How are children protected from potential dangers in their classroom? Page 126 could be used as a follow-up to this activity.

What kind of work? (Level 3)
❑ Using a section of *Yellow Pages* (BT), shade in a similar graph for the jobs listed. Do more people work as makers, diggers or helpers?

An industrial estate (Level 3)
❑ Carry out a survey of the factories near school. What are their names? What do they make?

Materials in cars (Level 3) Ensure that the children understand the range of materials used in making cars (steel, glass and plastic) and other objects, such as television sets or furniture.

Making cars (Level 4)
❏ Construct flow diagrams to show how other goods are made, such as furniture or paper.

Finding the best place: 1 (Level 5)
Discuss the need to locate the shop at a site where it can be reached by the maximum number of people. Factors such as accessibility and centrality are important. There is no one correct answer, the arguments put forward to justify each location are the essence of this activity.

Finding the best place: 2 (Level 5)
❏ If another new estate is built on the north side of the town, where would be the best place to open a second supermarket?

Leisure

In the park (Level 1)
❏ Carry out a survey of a local park. Record what jobs people do there and how the park is used.

Seaside (Level 1)
❏ Let the children draw a seaside place that they have visited and add the names of the different features, such as hotels and the beach.

Postcard from the coast (Level 2)
❏ The children could draw a mountain postcard scene and write about what they might have been doing there, such as hill-walking or horse riding.

Mapping the park (Level 2)
❏ Ask the children to draw a green line to show the route from the lake to the café and a yellow line from the picnic area to the lake and the toilets.

Winter in the mountains (Level 3)
❏ List other sports people might play here in winter.

Summer in the mountains (Level 3)
❏ List other sports people might play here in summer.

Spare time (Level 3)
Make sure the term 'leisure' is understood. Stress the need to include all activities (a two week period may be more appropriate).

❏ Let the children construct a database to find out which activities boys like the most, which girls like the most and which activity takes the longest time.

Using the park (Level 4)
❏ Carry out a survey of how people use a park near school. Ask what they most like and dislike about the park and how it could be improved.

Coastline (Level 4)
❏ Ask the children to add other features to the map and key, such as a large supermarket or a riding stable, and give reasons for the site they choose.

Time outdoors (Level 5)
Discuss how far people are prepared to travel for a half-day visit (summer 20–30km, winter 20km).

❏ Invent families whose members have different interests, such as birdwatching, walking or camping. Construct holiday routes for each family.

Getting around

Road signs (Level 1)
Make available a copy of the *Highway Code* DoT (1987) HMSO, together with posters from RoSPA (Cannon House, The Priory, Queensway, Birmingham B4 6BS) showing the main road signs.

Vehicles and drivers (Level 1)
❏ Use the children's drawings to prepare a wall display of vehicles that they see on nearby roads.

Today they saw on the road... (Level 2)
❏ Ask the children to draw pictures showing some of the things they saw on the road today.

Today I heard on the road... (Level 2)
❏ Ask the children to draw pictures showing some of the things they heard on the road today.

On the move (Level 3)
❏ Discuss the best type of transport for moving: diamonds from South Africa to England; cars from England to Belgium; flowers from the Netherlands to Scotland; whiskey from Ireland to England.

How far? (Level 3)
Discuss the difference between straight-line distances and real distances.

Motorway journeys (Level 3)
❏ Identify other motorway journeys, such as Exeter to Swansea, Liverpool to Glasgow and so on.

Journeys between North and South America (Level 3)
Ensure children are familiar with the main continents. Discuss the problems of travelling between the east and west coasts of North America before the railways were built.

❏ Ask the children show these journeys on their maps: Concepción to New York; Buenaventura to Vancouver; Vancouver to New York; Valparíso to San Fransisco; Rio de Janiero to Buenaventura.

Journeys through the Channel Tunnel (Level 4)
❏ How long will journeys take between Lisbon and Vienna, Barcelona and Rome, Newcastle and Stockholm, Manchester and Madrid.

Getting around town (Level 4)
Discuss the relative merits and drawbacks to each type of transport. The children's concept of the merits may vary with the location of their school. Suggest two locations, a big city like London and a smaller city like Milton Keynes.

Moving goods (Level 4)
Discuss the special requirements of heavy, valuable or bulky cargoes.

❏ Add other problems (moving the US President from Washington to London, cars from Germany to London and computers from Japan to Southampton).

Placing signs (Level 4)
Discuss the need to place signs where they are easily visible, close to the feature that they describe and where the sign will be encountered before the feature.

Milk round (Level 5)
❏ Add more streets to the map, then redesign Mr Page's route.

Building a motorway (Level 5)
Point out the value of a simple route taking as straight a path as possible.

Motorway debate (Level 5)
❏ Ask the children to draw on their maps any changes they would make to their routes as a result of hearing these local opinions.

Weather

Weather changes (Level 1)
❑ Ask the children to draw pictures to show a frosty day, a foggy day, a sunny day and a cloudy day.

A week's weather (Level 1)
❑ Ask what the weather was like on Friday afternoon and on Tuesday morning. Can the children explain how the weather changed during the day on Monday and on Tuesday?

This week's weather (Level 2)
The children will need to devise a series of weather symbols. It is useful to design one symbol for the weather condition, such as cloudy or foggy, and another for temperature, such as very cold, warm or hot.

Danger from the weather (Level 2)
❑ Ask the children to draw pictures on the back of the sheet to show what might have happened on Thursday and Friday because of the weather.

Different weather (Level 3)
❑ Challenge the children to draw pictures with clues to show that it has been raining for several days.

The right clothes (Level 3)
❑ Discuss how the clothes which the children wear change through a year.

Wind strength (Level 3)
❑ Look at the Beaufort scale for measuring wind. Draw pictures to show these wind conditions.

Recording the weather: rainfall (Level 3)
Let the children practise using a rain gauge. Show them examples of completed rainfall graphs.

Recording the weather: wind (Level 3)
The direction recorded is that from which the wind is blowing; a south-westerly wind is blowing from the south-west.

Recording the weather: temperature (Level 3)
This diagram should be drawn as a line graph, so explanation, practice and examples of other temperature graphs will be needed.

The weather forecast (Level 4)
❑ Ask the children to make up a summer forecast for the same areas and fill in blank UK maps (page 141) using their own symbols.

Problem weather (Level 4)
Discuss the problems weather causes for people and animals.
❑ Suggest how each problem might be solved.

Cloud types (Level 5)
❑ Let the children draw and identify some of the clouds they see over the course of a week. What type of weather did they bring?

Weathering (Level 5)
The commonest evidence of weathering is found on stone statues, brickwork on public buildings and tombstones.

Water

Water cycle (Level 1)
Stress that the process is a cycle within which the water circulates.

Living on an island (Level 1)
❑ List some of the similarities and differences between the picture and the school's local area.

Using water (Level 2)
❑ Ask the children to draw pictures of other uses of water and add these uses to their lists.

Water around us (Level 3)
Use photos and visits to explain what clues to water in the environment look like and clarify the function of each feature.
❑ Survey water signs and covers around school and mark their positions on a simple plan.

Keeping water out (Level 3)
❑ On a picture of a house in another country, label each part and explain how it helps to keep water out.

The world's rivers (Level 4)
❑ Use the blank world map (page 144) as the basis for drawing and labelling each river.

Uses of the river (Level 4)
❑ Add other uses of a river to your list and sort these into the same groups.

From source to sea (Level 4)
❑ Use an atlas to follow a British river from its source to its mouth and list the towns it passes through.

River at work (Level 5)
Use a sand tray and watering-can to show how rivers form on sloping surfaces, remove (erode) and transport material and then deposit it lower down. Increasing/decreasing the speed and/or volume of water flow shows how the river shape changes during floods or drought.

Flooding: for and against (Level 5)
❑ Consider the opinions of the owner of the local quarry and the members of the sailing club about these proposed changes to the river.

In the country

The countryside (Level 1)
Discuss the names for key geographical features, such as hill, valley and stream. Have a model farm in the classroom as a reference point for items such as fences and barns and for the different types of animals.

Food from the countryside (Level 1)
❑ Let the children draw other foods they enjoy and, alongside, where they come from.

Brooke Farm (Level 1)
❑ Ask the children how many cows there are in the field and tell them to draw 15 sheep in another field.

A plan of Brooke Farm (Level 2)
Make sure the children understand the idea of plan view here.
❑ Tell the children that after the fields have grown grass, the next year they are planted with sugar beet. How many fields will grow sugar beet next year?

The journey of milk (Level 2)
Make sure that the children understand what each picture shows.
❑ Encourage them to describe, verbally and in writing, how milk gets from cows to our homes.

Hill farming (Level 2)
❑ Ask which field is nearest and which is furthest.

Seasonal jobs: 1 and 2 (Level 3)
Explain the types of work carried out on a farm, from ploughing to sheep shearing, and how the range of work varies with the type of farm. The concept of how work varies over the seasons is easier to establish but still needs to be

related to the type of farm, for example harvesting crops on an arable farm in the autumn.

Food from other countries (Level 3) A collection of labels from a variety of foods (canned, frozen, dried or tinned) and a range of countries ensures that children grasp the idea of interdependence.

Streamside Farm (Level 4) This is an example of an arable farm and can be used for comparison with the hill farm on page 117.

Changes in farming (Level 5) Develop ideas about the effects of farming on wildlife through the loss of hedgerows, ponds and other habitats.

Farming decisions (Level 5) Make sure that the principles of time and distance are understood.

The environment

Spoiling the river (Level 1)
❏ Discuss how the river in the picture or a local polluted pond or stream could be cleaned up.

Improving our environment (Level 2) Encourage the children not just to think about what things will improve the playground, but also the best location for each feature, for example jumping castles need to be away from flower beds.

Dangers in the environment (Level 3)
❏ Make a survey of the potential dangers in school and discuss how they could be prevented.

Using and reusing (Level 3) A bag of teacher-selected 'rubbish' could be discussed before starting this activity. Children should describe each item and say how it might be reused in its present form, such as old pencils, or whether it should be recycled.

Volcano (Level 4) Ensure understanding of what happens when a volcano erupts and how the cone is developed. Read out eye-witness descriptions.

Earthquake (Level 4)
❏ How could the problems created by the earthquake be solved? (Airlifts of warm clothing.)
❏ List these responses, starting with the most urgent.

Surveying the streets (Level 4) Give guidance in making judgements about each of the features. Note that the higher the score the better the street.
❏ Choose (three) other features to add to the list of street conditions.

A change for the better (Level 4)
❏ Study two photographs of an area near the school taken 30 or 40 years apart. What things have not changed? Has the area been improved?

Consequences (Level 5)
❏ Study a proposed change in your local environment, such as a new road. Which groups of people are in favour and which groups are against?

Living in India

A village in India (Level 1) You will need additional resources before encouraging children to attempt this and the following activities. Some useful resources include:
- *Chembakolli, a Village in India* (ActionAid, 1991) an activity photopack;
- *Geography – Start Here!* (Central ITV) television series including comparative references to and one whole programme concerning life in an Indian village, accompanied by *Geography – Start Here!* (1992, Collins Educational) photopack. These books and videos are available from the Educational Television Company, PO Box 100, Warwick CV34 6TZ.

Using water in India (Level 1)
❏ List all the ways in which we use water in Britain. Divide the list into 'Things to do with drinking', 'Things to do with washing' and 'Other uses'.

A letter to India (Level 2) Before attempting this activity, discuss the sequence of events between writing and posting a letter.

Chanda's day (Level 3)
❏ Add other activities, such as sweeping the floor, eating and relaxing. Discuss when and for how long Chanda would do these additional activities.

My day (Level 3) This sheet is designed to be compared with 'Chanda's day' (page 136).
❏ Ask the children to each complete one blank clock diagram for a weekday and one for a weekend. What are the main similarities and differences?

A meal in India (Level 3)
❏ List everything the class eats over 24 hours, then add these items to the correct columns of the table.

The weather in Delhi (Level 4) Make it clear that rainfall is recorded as a bar graph.

Village life (Level 5) Stress that many people are happy with village life in India and that for some people it has advantages over life in the UK. While there are 'problems', these should not be overstated.

Maps

The United Kingdom Ensure familiarity with names and places by referring to atlas maps as often as possible and asking the children to mark and name features on copies of this outline, such as rivers, towns, counties and the surrounding seas.

Europe: 1 Refer children to atlas maps of Europe. Ask them to mark and name on the outline map countries, capital cities, rivers and seas

Europe: 2 (Latitude and longitude) Explain that lines of latitude increase northwards and southwards away from the Equator and lines of longitude increase east and west from 0°, which runs through Greenwich. Explain the use of these imaginary lines as a grid for accurately locating places. Show, using a globe, how the lines may seem curved on maps because of the curvature of the earth's surface. Stress that in giving latitude and longitude references, the first number always indicates the degrees north or south of the Equator, while the second number indicates the degrees east or west of Greenwich.

The world Encourage the children to become familiar with the continents, major rivers and cities.

Attainment target charts

Attainment target chart (1)

Target ability level	Page	Name of activity	AT1	AT2	AT3	AT4	AT5
1	11	Where?	✓				
	12	Where things are	✓				
	13	Symbols	✓				
	14	Buildings as symbols	✓				
	15	Plans	✓				
	16	Toy plans	✓				
	17	The neighbourhood	✓				
2	18	Left and right	✓				
	19	In the maze	✓				
	20	Joanne's bedroom	✓				
	21	Routes around school	✓				
	22	Routes through town	✓				
	23	Keys on maps and plans	✓				
3	24	Directions	✓				
	25	Following directions	✓				
	26	On the shelf	✓				
	27	Finding things	✓				
	28	The United Kingdom	✓				
	29	Compass points	✓				
	30	Grids and symbols	✓				
	31	Four-figure grid references	✓				
	32	Distances	✓				
4	33	Aeroplane travel	✓				
	34	Routes to school	✓				
	35	Europe	✓				
	36	Towns and countries in Europe					
5	37	Six-figure grid references	✓				
	38	Modelling contours	✓				
	39	Up and down	✓				
	40	A contour map	✓				
	41	Holiday snaps	✓				
1	42	Lucy's house			✓		
	43	Building materials			✓		

Attainment target chart (2)

Target ability level	Page	Name of activity	AT1	AT2	AT3	AT4	AT5
2	44	Going shopping				✓	
	45	Different homes		✓		✓	
3	46	Under our feet		✓		✓	
	47	People on the move				✓	
	48	Different types of town				✓	
	49	City centre		✓		✓	
4	50	Different land uses				✓	
	51	The changing street		✓		✓	
	52	Developing the area				✓	
5	53	People who help us				✓	
1	54	Problems of quarrying				✓	✓
	55	Opencast coal-mining				✓	
	56	Work dangers				✓	✓
3	57	What kind of work?				✓	
	58	An industrial estate				✓	
	59	Materials in cars				✓	
4	60	Making cars				✓	
5	61	Finding the best place: 1				✓	
	62	Finding the best place: 2				✓	
1	63	In the park				✓	
	64	Seaside			✓		
2	65	Postcard from the coast			✓		
	66	Mapping at the park	✓			✓	
3	67	Winter in the mountains			✓	✓	
	68	Summer in the mountains			✓	✓	
4	69	Spare time				✓	
	70	Using the park				✓	
5	71	Coastline				✓	
	72	Time outdoors				✓	
1	73	Road signs				✓	
	74	Vehicles and drivers				✓	
2	75	Today they saw on the road...				✓	
	76	Today they heard on the road...				✓	

Attainment target chart (3)

Target ability level	Page	Name of activity	AT1	AT2	AT3	AT4	AT5
3	77	On the move	✓				
	78	How far?	✓				
	79	Motorway journeys	✓				
	80	Journeys between North and South America		✓			
4	81	Journeys through the Channel Tunnel				✓	
	82	Getting around town				✓	
	83	Moving goods				✓	
5	84	Placing signs	✓				
	85	Milk round	✓				
	86	Building a motorway	✓			✓	
	87	Motorway debate				✓	✓
1	88	Weather changes			✓		
	89	A week's weather			✓	✓	
2	90	This week's weather	✓			✓	
	91	Danger from the weather				✓	
	92	Different weather			✓	✓	
	93	The right clothes				✓	
	94	Wind strength			✓	✓	
3	95	Recording the weather: rainfall	✓			✓	
	96	Recording the weather: wind	✓			✓	✓
	97	Recording the weather: temperature	✓			✓	✓
4	98	Weather forecast	✓		✓	✓	
	99	Problem weather	✓			✓	
5	100	Cloud types	✓				
	101	Weathering			✓		
1	102	Water cycle			✓		
	103	Living on an island			✓		
2	104	Using water		✓			
	105	Water around us		✓	✓		
3	106	Keeping water out			✓	✓	

Attainment target chart (4)

Target ability level	Page	Name of activity	AT1	AT2	AT3	AT4	AT5
4	107	The world's rivers					✓
	108	Uses of the river		✓	✓		
	109	From source to sea			✓		
5	110	River at work		✓	✓	✓	
	111	Flooding: for and against				✓	
1	112	The countryside			✓		
	113	Food from the countryside		✓		✓	
2	114	Brooke Farm	✓				
	115	A plan of Brooke Farm	✓			✓	
	116	The journey of milk		✓		✓	
	117	Hill farming			✓	✓	
3	118	Seasonal jobs: 1			✓		
	119	Seasonal jobs: 2			✓		
	120	Food from other countries		✓		✓	
4	121	Streamside Farm		✓	✓		
	122	Changes in farming		✓		✓	✓
5	123	Farming decisions		✓		✓	
1	124	Spoiling the river		✓	✓	✓	✓
	125	Improving our environment				✓	✓
2	126	Dangers in the environment				✓	✓
3	127	Using and reusing		✓		✓	✓
	128	Volcano			✓		
	129	Earthquake			✓		
4	130	Surveying the streets	✓	✓			
	131	A change for the better		✓		✓	
5	132	Consequences		✓		✓	✓
1	133	A village in India		✓		✓	✓
	134	Using water in India		✓		✓	
2	135	A letter to India		✓		✓	✓
	136	Chanda's day		✓		✓	✓
3	137	My day		✓		✓	✓
	138	A meal in India		✓		✓	
4	139	The weather in Delhi		✓	✓		✓
5	140	Village life		✓		✓	✓

Name _____

Where?

❖ Draw lines to match each picture with its opposite.

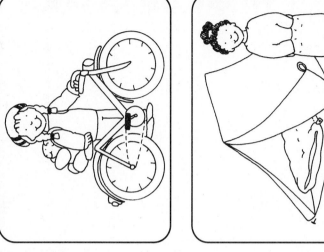
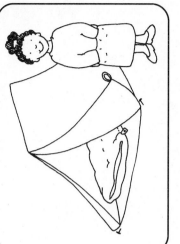

❖ Now draw some more opposites.

Where things are

Where things are

- ❖ Look at the picture below.
- ❖ Draw a block of flats next to the factory.
- ❖ Draw a van in front of the factory.
- ❖ Draw a tree next to the church.
- ❖ Draw a duck on the pond.

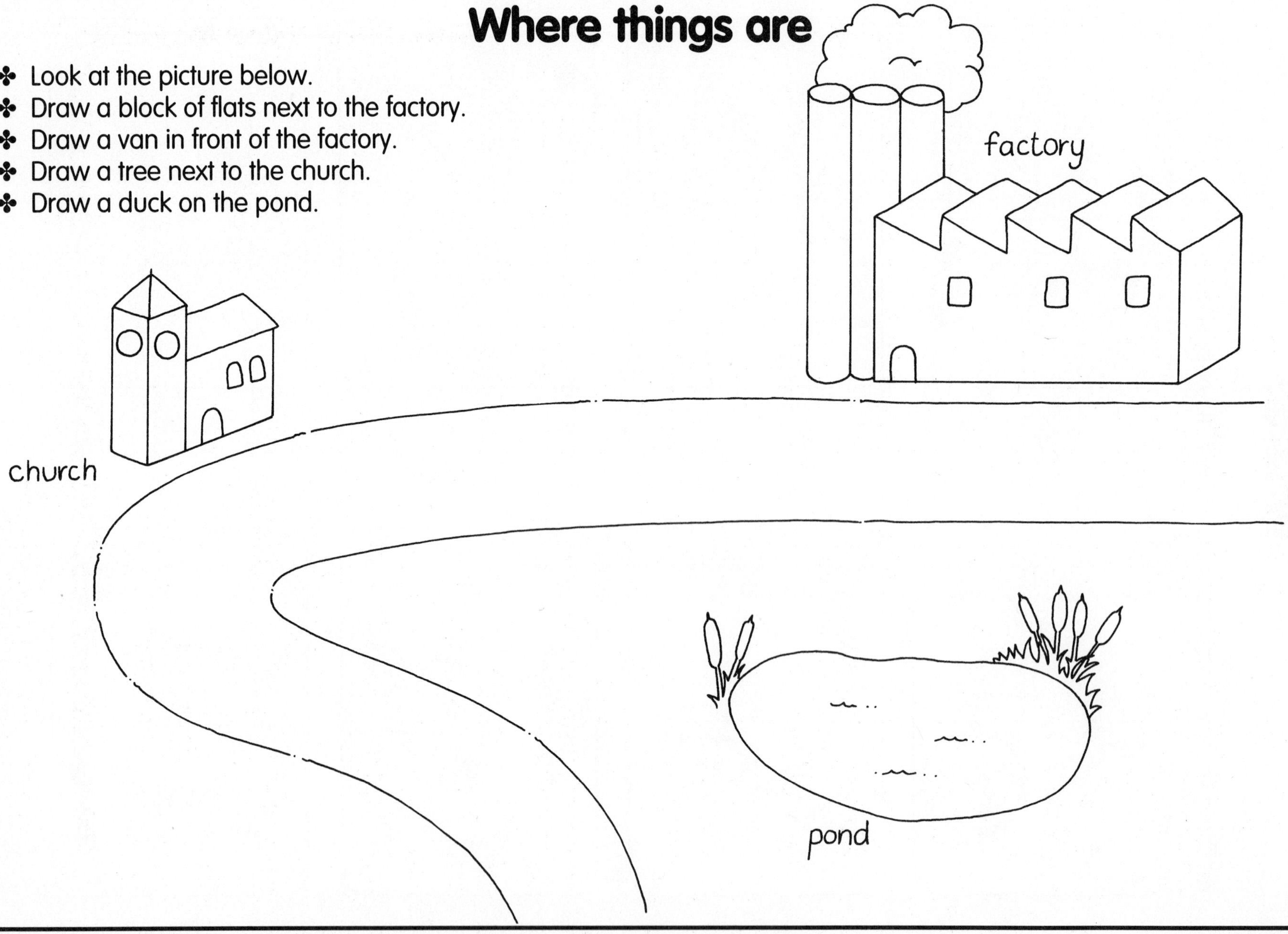

factory

church

pond

Name _____

Symbols

Each of the symbols below means something.
We can use them to send secret messages.

✔	✗	no
yes		
☀ sun	☁ cloudy	
	sunny	
🌳 woods	🌳 cloud	pond
╱╲	┆┆	
railway line		road

✶ Write in the spaces what each symbol means in these messages.

● "It is ☀ today."

● "I will meet you by the ☁ ."

● "The ╱╲ is busy."

● "The ┆┆ leads to the school."

✤ Now make up your own symbols.

Geography

13

Name _____

Buildings as symbols

Sapria and Mike have been making a survey of the buildings in their part of town.
✤ In each box draw a symbol for the type of building they saw.
Make sure that the symbols show clearly the different types of building.

school	bank	factory
cinema	hotel	hospital

Geography

Plans

Plans show things as they look when seen from above.

♣ Match each picture with its plan view by shading them both in the same colour.

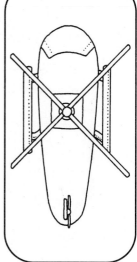
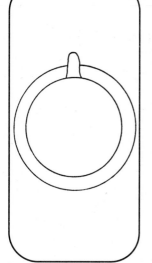
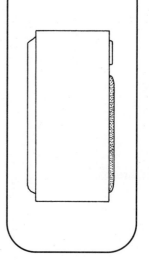
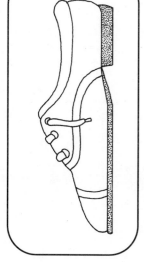
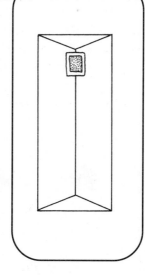

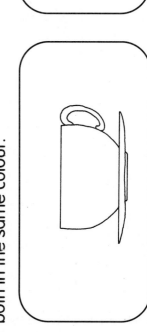
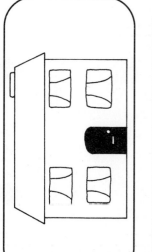
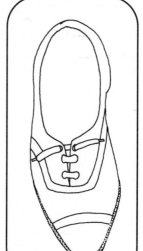

Toy plans

Toy plans

This is a collection of children's toys.

Here is a plan of part of the toy collection.

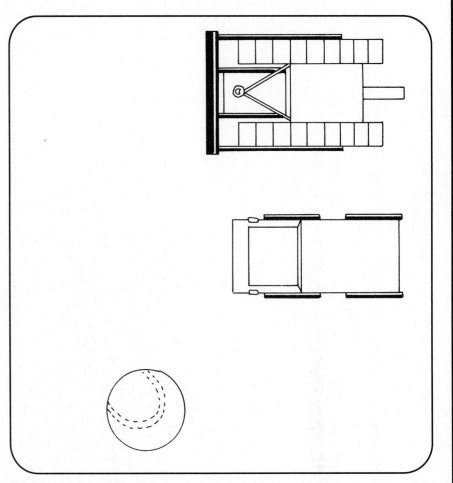

❖ Match each toy with its plan view by shading them both the same colour.
❖ Some toys in the collection are not shown on the plan. Draw in the plan views of the missing toys.

The neighbourhood

This is a picture of a neighbourhood.

Here is a plan view of the neighbourhood.

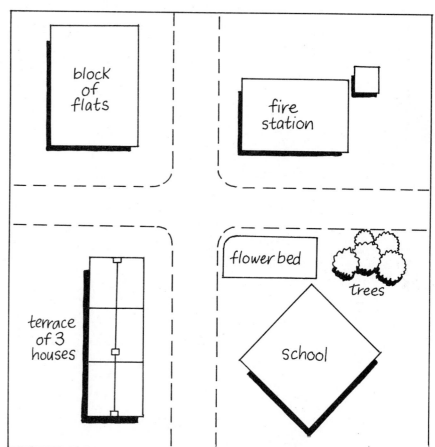

❖ Colour in these things on the picture and the plan:
- the school in blue;
- the flats in yellow;
- the fire station in red;
- the trees in green;
- the flower bed in brown.

Name _____

Left and right

Left and right

❖ Look at these children.
❖ Colour their left arms and left legs in green.
❖ Colour their right legs and right arms in red.

In the maze

Abena has to find her way through the maze to Sally.

❧ Draw a red line to show her path through the maze.

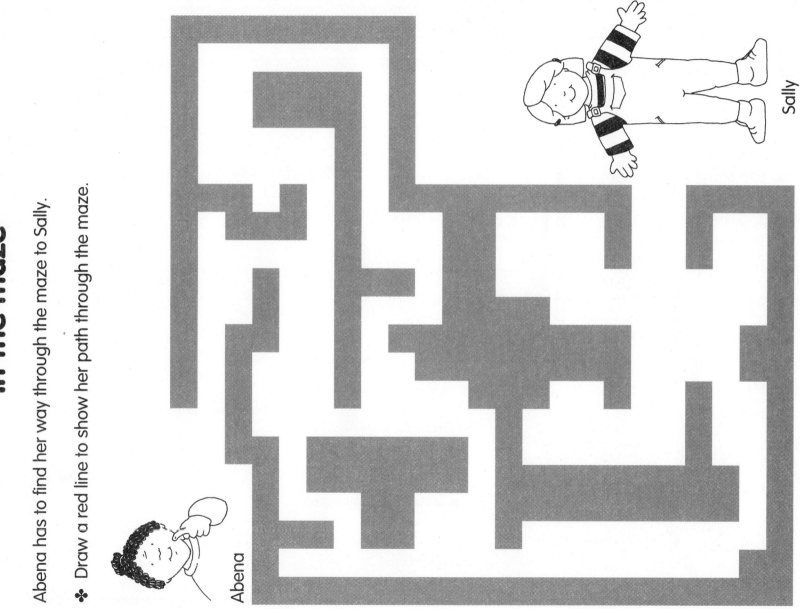

Abena

Sally

❧ How many times does she turn left?
❧ How many times does she turn right?

Name _____

Joanne's bedroom

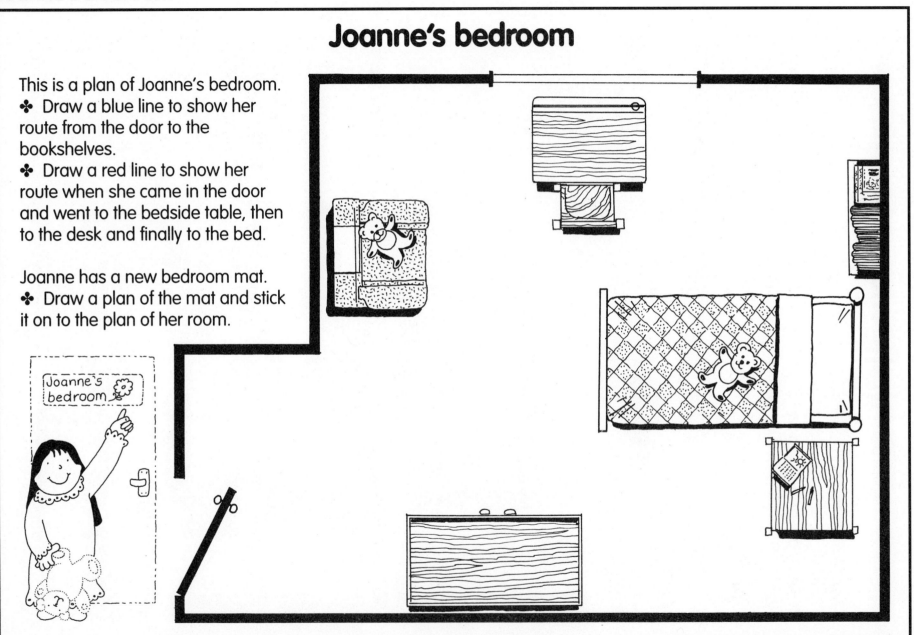

Joanne's bedroom

This is a plan of Joanne's bedroom.
❖ Draw a blue line to show her route from the door to the bookshelves.
❖ Draw a red line to show her route when she came in the door and went to the bedside table, then to the desk and finally to the bed.

Joanne has a new bedroom mat.
❖ Draw a plan of the mat and stick it on to the plan of her room.

Geography

Name _____

Routes around school

This is a map of Broadview Primary School.

♣ Draw a green line to show the route from classroom 1 to the hall.
♣ Draw a red line to show the route from classroom 6 to the medical room.
♣ Draw a blue line to show the route from classroom 2 to the staff room.

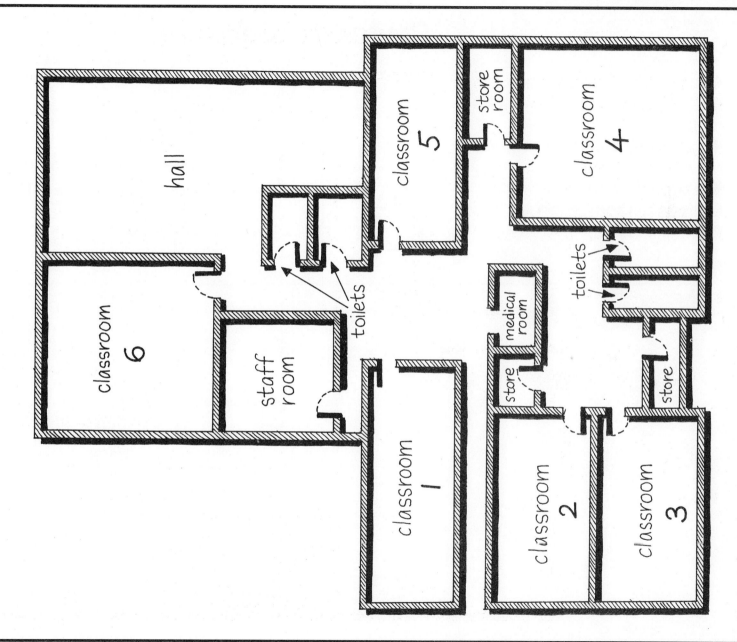

Geography

Name _____

Routes through town

Routes through town

✤ Look at the plan opposite.
✤ Draw a red line to show Brett's route to school.
✤ List the things Brett passes on his way to school.
✤ Draw a blue line to show how Brett can get from school to Rashni's house.

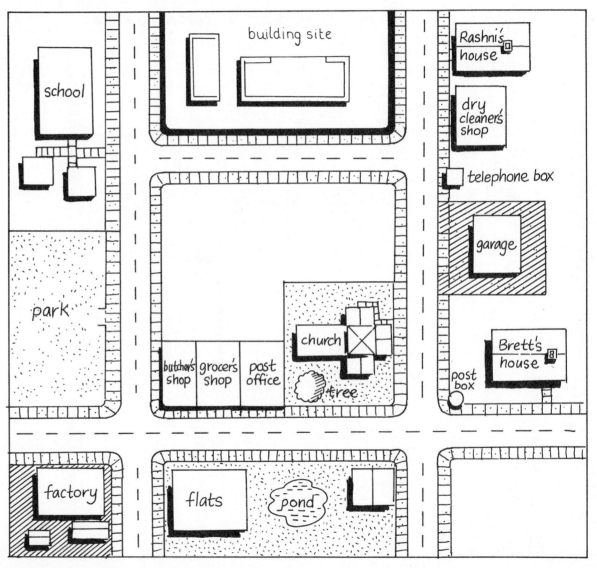

Name _____

Keys on maps and plans

This is a plan of Sandra's garden. It shows which crops she grows where.

✤ Think of a symbol for each of the crops. Draw each symbol on the plan to show where that crop is grown.

✤ Make a key to show what the symbols mean.

p		pears	a		apples
pe		peas	c		cabbages
pl		plums	b		beans
po		potatocs	s		sprouts
		path			shed

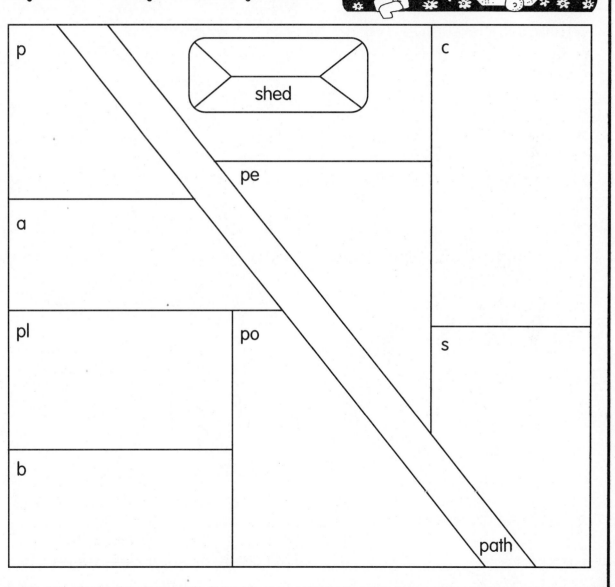

Name _____

Directions

Directions

✤ Look at this drawing of a village. The lake is **east** of the hotel.

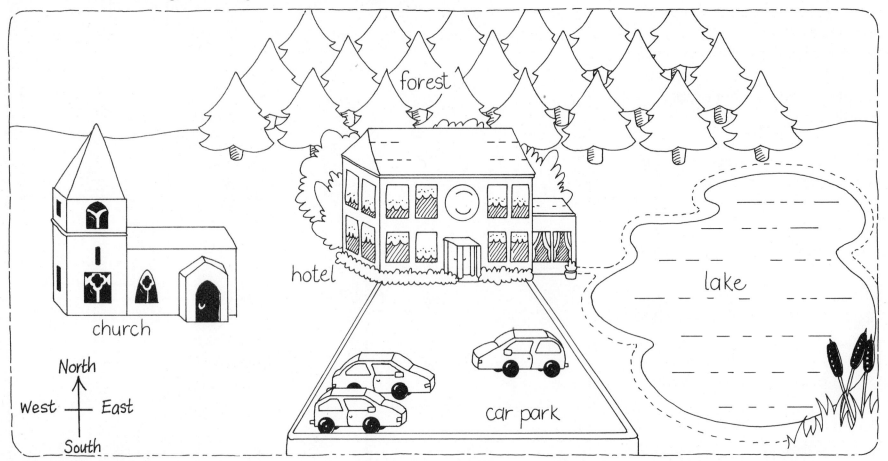

✤ Complete these sentences.

• The church is _____ of the hotel.

• The _____ is north of the hotel.

• The car park is _____ of the hotel.

Name _____

Following directions

Martin is ill. The ambulance is going to his house. This is the route it takes:
East along Oak Street; then north along Winchester Drive; then east along
Lime Way; then north along Eton Drive; then east along Shaw Lane.

❖ Draw the route on the plan below.

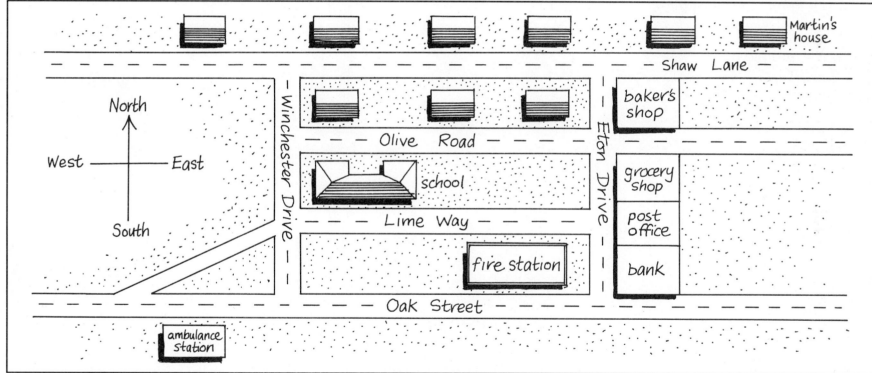

❖ Is the bank north or south
of the post office?

❖ Is the fire station east or
west of the bank?

❖ Is the bank east or west
of the fire station?

_____

_____

_____

Name _____

On the shelf

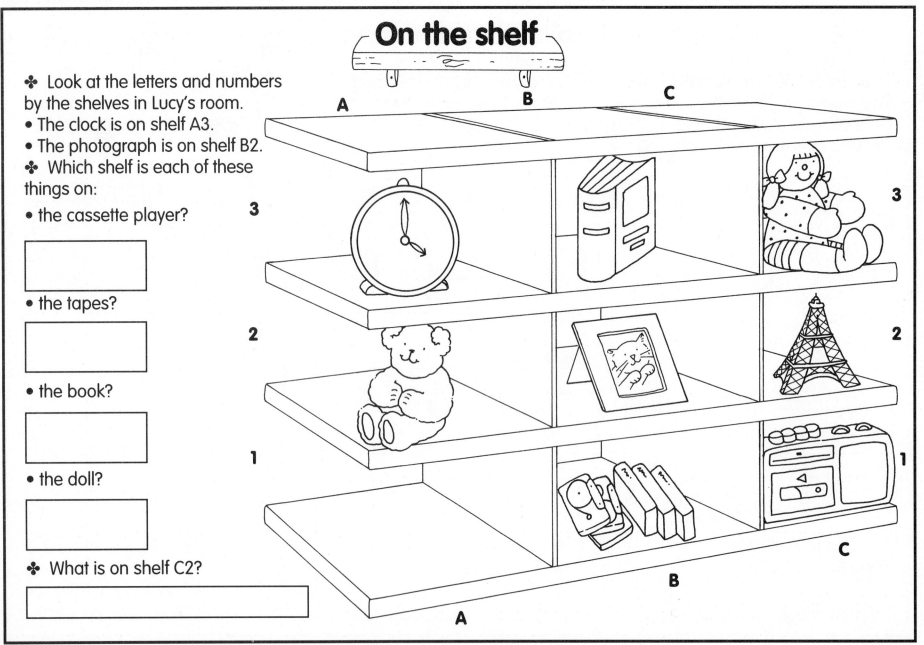

❖ Look at the letters and numbers by the shelves in Lucy's room.
- The clock is on shelf A3.
- The photograph is on shelf B2.

❖ Which shelf is each of these things on:
- the cassette player?

- the tapes?

- the book?

- the doll?

❖ What is on shelf C2?

Name _____

   # Finding things

Grids can be used to find the position of things.
❖ Look at the grid below.
• The ball is in square D2.

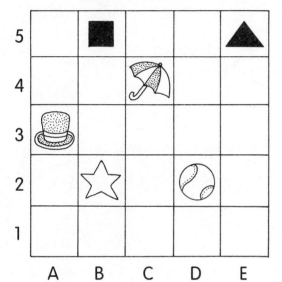

❖ Draw these things on the grid below:
• a fish in D3;   • a street-lamp in B3;   • a car in G8;
• a bus in F6;   • a television in C7;   • a house in A5.

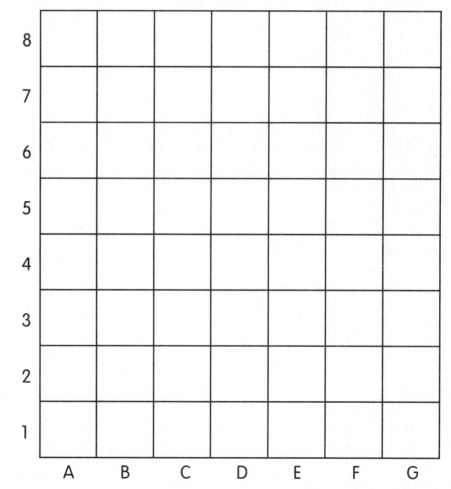

❖ Complete these sentences.

• The black triangle is in square _____

• The black square is in square _____

• The star is in square _____

• The hat is in square _____

• The umbrella is in square _____

The United Kingdom

Name _____

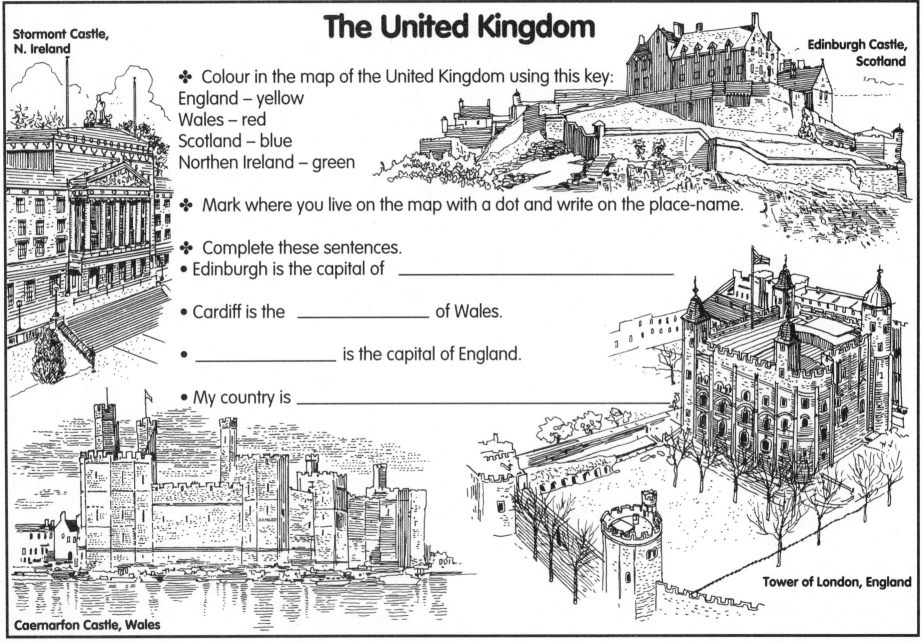

Stormont Castle, N. Ireland

Edinburgh Castle, Scotland

The United Kingdom

❖ Colour in the map of the United Kingdom using this key:

England – yellow
Wales – red
Scotland – blue
Northen Ireland – green

❖ Mark where you live on the map with a dot and write on the place-name.

❖ Complete these sentences.
• Edinburgh is the capital of _____

• Cardiff is the _____ of Wales.

• _____ is the capital of England.

• My country is _____

Tower of London, England

Caernarfon Castle, Wales

Geography

Name _____

Compass points

We use a compass to find where places are located.
This compass shows eight directions.

♣ Use the compass to fill in the missing directions below.

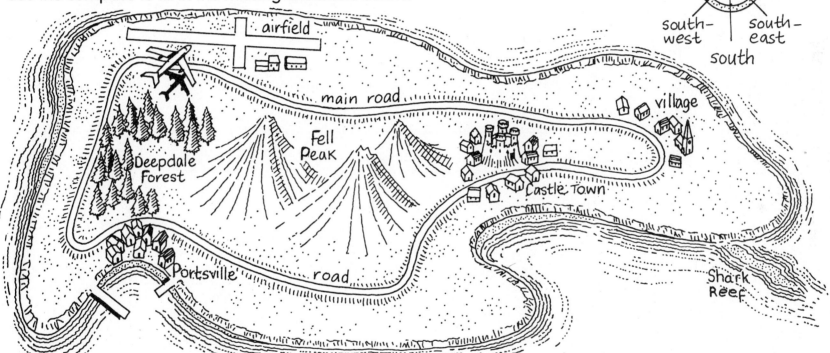

Fell Peak is north-east of Portsville

• The airfield is _____ of Fell Peak.

• Deepdale Forest is _____ of Portsville.

• Castle Town is _____ of Portsville.

• Shark Reef is _____ of Castle Town.

• Castle Town is _____ of the village.

Name _____

Grids and symbols

Grids and symbols

✤ Use the symbols in the key and the following information
to complete the map.
● The coast runs through A4, B4, C4, C3, D3, D2, C2, C1 and B1.
● There are cliffs and flat rocks in C4, C3 and D3.
● There are sand hills in C1 and B1.
● There is mud in A4 and B4 and sand in D2.
● There is a lighthouse on the cliffs in D3 and a windmill in B2.
✤ Use your own symbols to add the following features to the map.
● The river winds through A2, A3, B2, B3 to an estuary in B4.
● There is a waterfall in B2.
✤ Remember to put your new symbols on to the key.

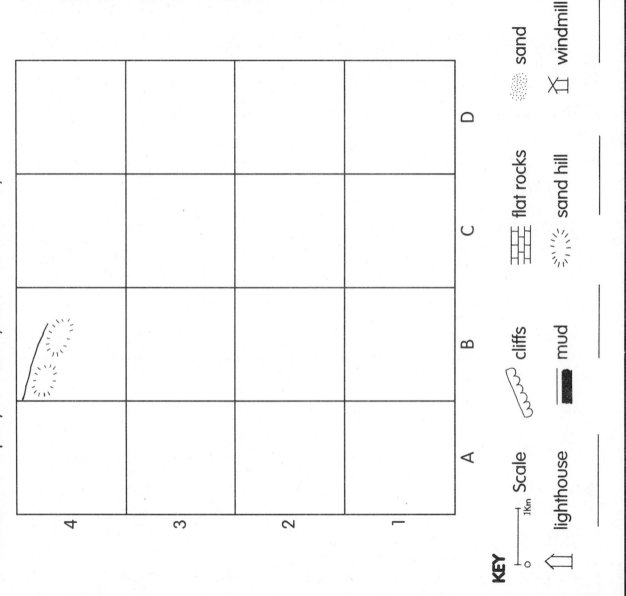

KEY

Scale ├─┤ 1Km
0

⇦ lighthouse

〰 cliffs   ▦ flat rocks   ⸫ sand

▬ mud   ☀ sand hill   ✕ windmill

Four-figure grid references

❖ Look at the map below. What can be found in each of these squares? References always give the number along the bottom of the grid first and then up the side. For example, the reference for Seal Bay is 2258.

2257 _____   2659 _____   2559 _____

2558 _____   2657 _____   2160 _____

2459 _____   2357 _____   2560 _____

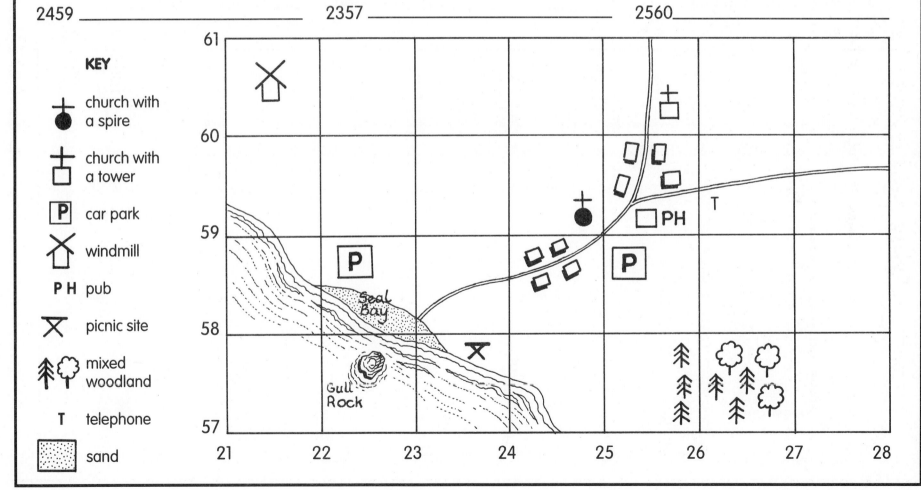

KEY

church with a spire

church with a tower

P car park

windmill

P H pub

picnic site

mixed woodland

T telephone

sand

Name _____

Distances

✤ Look at the map below. 1 centimetre represents 10 metres.

✤ Work out the following distances:

• from Ravi's house to the bank _____

• from Ravi's house to the garage _____

• from Ravi's house to the lake _____

• from Ravi's house to the school _____

✤ How far is the garage from the bank? _____

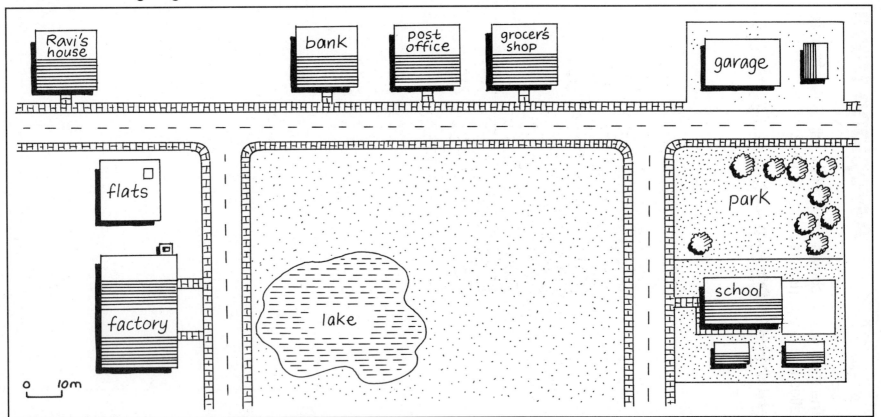

Name _____

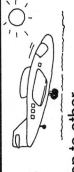

Aeroplane travel

The map below shows some of the air routes from London to other cities in Britain. (1cm represents 100 km.)

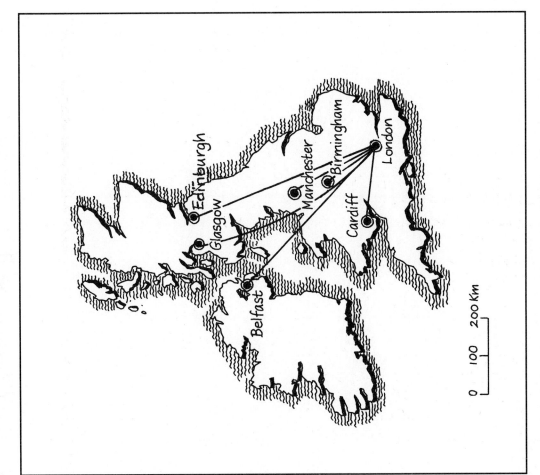

✦ Measure the distances between each pair of cities and complete this chart.

Start	Finish	Map distance in cm	Distance in km
London	Birmingham	1.5 cm	150 km
London	Cardiff		
London	Manchester		
London	Glasgow		
London	Belfast		
London	Edinburgh		

Name _____

Routes to school

Routes to school

The map below shows the area around Westfield Primary School.

♣ Using different colours, draw in the routes that Paul, Jane, Rashni and Ali take from home to school.

This is Paul's description of his route to school.

'I leave our house and turn right into Mill Lane. The road joins Barn Road, then I pass the mosque on my right. I turn left into High Street opposite the playing fields and cross the railway bridge, then the school is on my right.'

♣ What did Paul forget to mention?

♣ Now write similar descriptions of the things that Jane, Rashni and Ali see on their way to school.

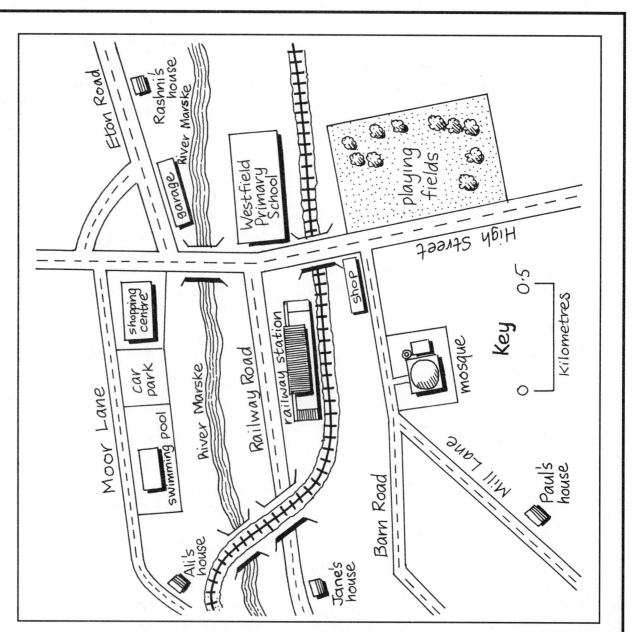

Europe

❖ Using the map of Europe to help you, find out the information required to fill in this sheet.

• Name three countries with a Mediterranean coast.

• Name four countries with a North Sea coast.

• Complete the table of countries and capitals below.

Capital	Country
London	England
Paris	
	Denmark
Lisbon	
	Spain
Berlin	
	Scotland
Athens	

Name _____

Towns and countries in Europe

Lines of latitude and longitude help us to find where places are located on a globe. The first number tells us how many degrees north of the equator the place is. The second number tell us how many degrees east or west of 0° the place is. For example, Paris is 49°N 2°E.

❖ Look at the latitude and longitude map of Europe.
- Which towns are at these references:

    41°N 4°W _____

    51°N 0° _____

    52°N 5°E _____

- What are the references for:

    Rome _____

    Berlin _____

    Copenhagen _____

- In which country would you be at these locations:

    45°N 5°E _____

    50°N 10°E _____

    45°N 10°E _____

Six-figure grid references

To give a six figure grid reference first read the easting. For example, for the church with the tower on the grid below the easting is 21. Then estimate the tenths eastwards (5). This is the third figure and gives you 215. Now read the northing (56), then estimate the tenths northwards (5). This is the sixth figure.
The six-figure reference is:

<u>215</u>   <u>565</u>

easting   northing

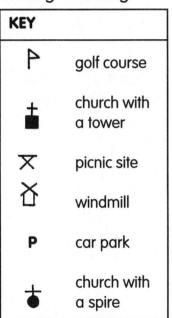

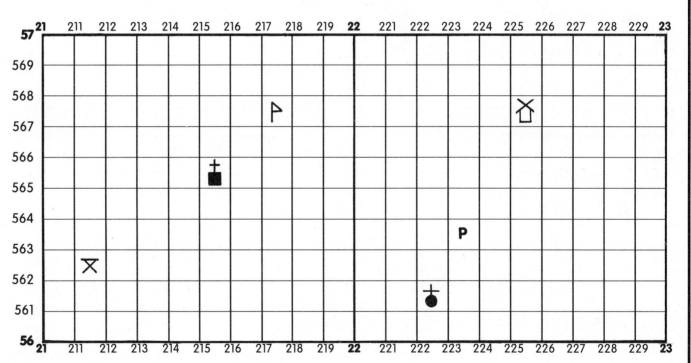

✤ Complete these references.

• The church with a spire is at 222 _____   • The car park is at _____ 563   • The windmill is at _____

✤ What is at grid reference 217 567? _____   ✤ What is at grid reference 211 562?_____

Modelling contours

Modelling contours

What you need: modelling clay; a piece of card; a transparent, water-tight tank; a ruler; a measuring jug; a sharp pencil or clay-modelling tool; a pencil and a piece of paper.

• Make a model of a hill using the modelling clay on a piece of card.

• Put your model in the tank.

• Pour in water until it is 3cm deep. Mark a line round the hill to show where the water reaches.

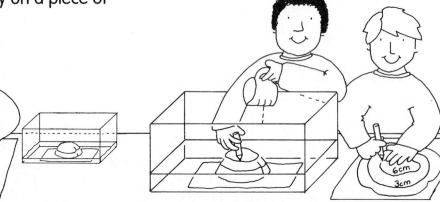

• Draw a map of your hill including the line of the water. This line is a **contour line** which shows the vertical height of the hill at this level.

• Pour in another 3cm depth of water. Mark a second line round the hill where the water now reaches. Draw a new map of the hill with the 3cm and 6cm contours marked.

• Continue increasing the depth of the water in 3cm steps until the hill is covered. Draw a new map each time. Your final map should look something like this one.

Up and down

❖ Look at the map below, then answer the following questions.

• Name three things in the valley?   • What is the western hill called?   • What is the eastern hill called?

_____   _____   _____

❖ If you cycled from Ring Church to Newfield School which part of your journey
would be uphill, AB or BC? _____ Which part would be downhill? _____

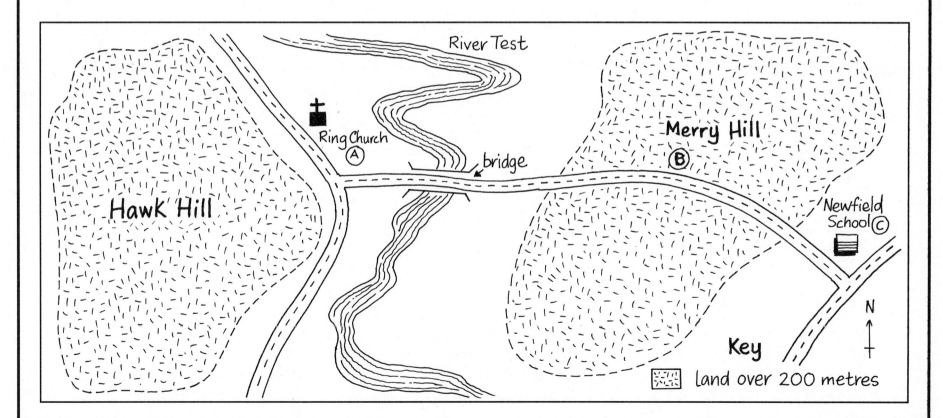

River Test

Ring Church
Ⓐ

bridge

Merry Hill
Ⓑ

Hawk Hill

Newfield
School Ⓒ

N

Key

land over 200 metres

Name _____

A contour map

A contour map

Contours are lines that show the height of the land.
❧ Look at this map and then answer the following questions.

• Which building is on the highest land?

• What is at sea level?

• At what height is the church with a tower?

• At what height is the picnic spot?

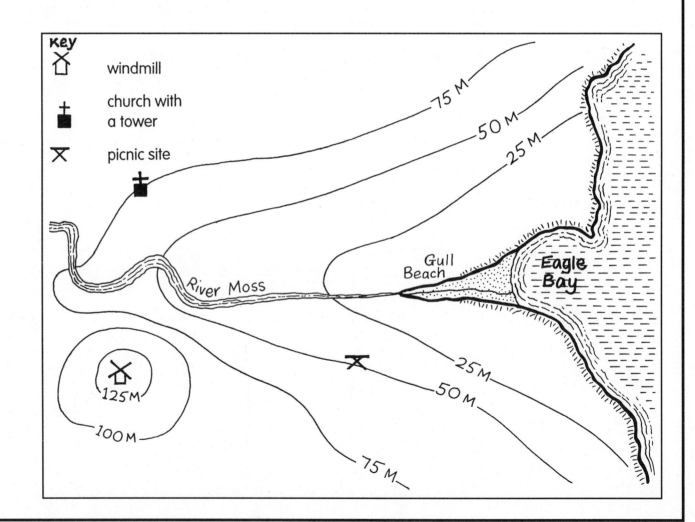

Name _____

Holiday snaps

Here is a map of a place that Tom and Emma visited on holiday.

Below are some of the photographs they took while they were there.

❖ Mark on the map the places where you think the three 'holiday snaps' were taken.

❖ Draw a picture of what you would see from point A looking west.

Lucy's house

Name _____

Lucy's house

✤ Look at this picture of Lucy's house. Choose a label from the ones below to write in each box.

✤ Draw a picture of your house. Label each room.

roof

living room

kitchen

bedroom

front door

bathroom

Building materials

❖ Look at these houses. What materials have been used to build them?
❖ Write the labels given in the correct boxes on the picture.

glass

plastic

wood

brick

tile

Going shopping

Name _____

Going shopping

❧ Look at the shopping list on the right.
❧ Write each item on the picture in front of the shop where you would buy it.

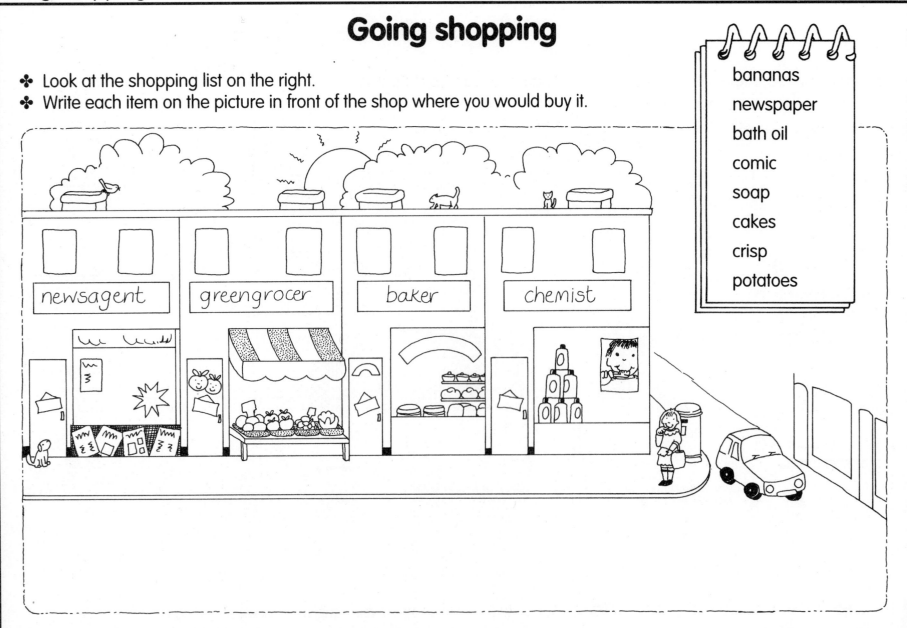

bananas

newspaper

bath oil

comic

soap

cakes

crisp

potatoes

newsagent   greengrocer   baker   chemist

Different homes

❖ Label each of the pictures below using the correct word from the list.

detached
bungalow
flats
maisonettes
caravan
terraced
semi-detached

❖ Carry out a class survey to find out how many children live in each different type of home.

Name _____

Under our feet

Under our feet

This picture shows that lots of activities go on beneath our feet.

❖ Draw a circle round all the clues you can spot to things which are going on underground.

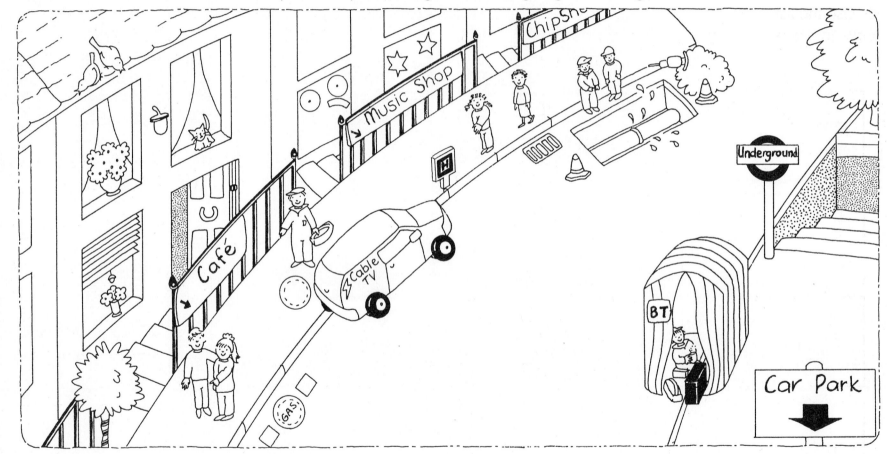

❖ Carry out a survey in a street near your school.
How many clues can you find there to activities going on under your feet?

People on the move

When people retire they often decide to move house. Many go to live in places near to the coast or in the countryside.

♣ Use the list opposite to fill in the boxes below to show which factors 'push' people to leave towns and which 'pull' them to the coast.

Leaving towns

Arriving at the coast

- sea views

- noisy streets

- busy traffic

- fresh air

- more people of the same age

- fear of crime

- crowded buses and trains

- homes and flats for senior citizens

'Push' factors

'Pull' factors

Name _____

Different types of towns

Different types of towns

Different towns are important for different things. We can often tell
what is special about a town from pictures like the ones below.
❖ Choose a label from the list to write in the box under each town picture.
❖ On a separate sheet of paper explain the reasons for your choices.

> **a capital city**
>
> **a holiday resort**
>
> **a market town**
>
> **a port**
>
> **an industrial town**

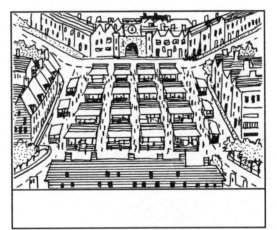

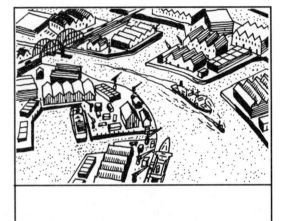

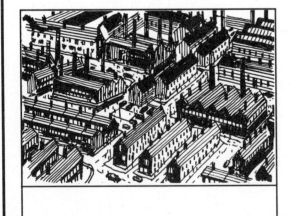

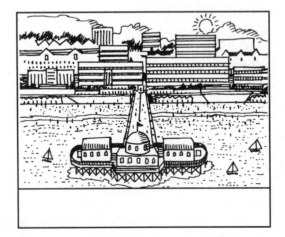

City centre

❖ Colour in this picture of a city centre using the key opposite.

transport	–	brown
offices	–	blue
shops	–	yellow
recreation	–	green
homes	–	red
others	–	purple

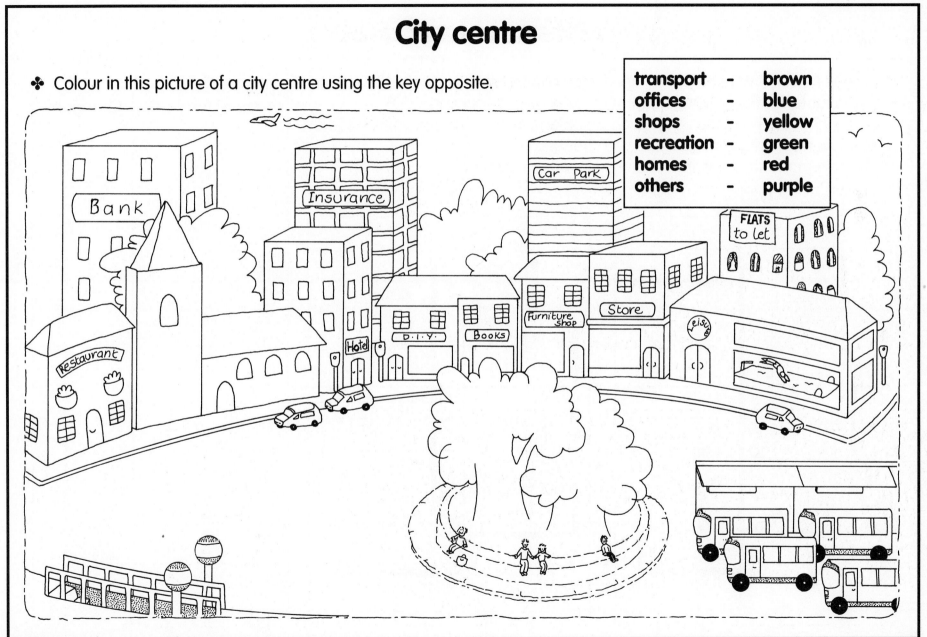

Different land uses

Different land uses

The maps below show part of a village in 1930 and the same part in 1993.
✤ In the table, list the buildings and other uses of land found in 1930
and in 1993. Put a tick if the use has changed and a cross if it has not changed.
• On how many sites has the land use changed?
• On how many sites has the land use stayed the same?

Type of land use	Changed?

1930

1993

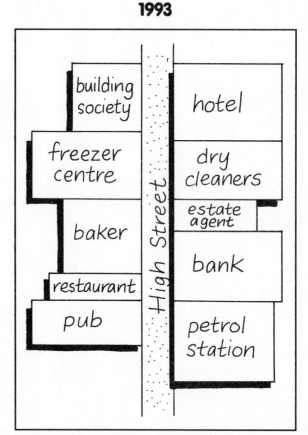

Name _____

The changing street

The two pictures below show the same street near a town centre. Changes have been made.
❖ List all the changes you can see and say why you think each change was made.

Change	Reasons for change

Name _____

Developing the area

Developing the area

The four sites shown on the plan below are ready for development.
Each site is described opposite.

✤ Decide which of these developments best suits each of the sites:
- multi-storey car park;
- superstore;
- housing estate;
- industrial estate.

✤ Mark each development on the plan at the site of your choice.

✤ Explain your choices on the back of this sheet.

Site 1: old shops, can be demolished for rebuilding.

Site 2: lots of open space, an attractive area.

Site 3: large site near motorway.

Site 4: rough ground, used to be a timberyard, factories around it.

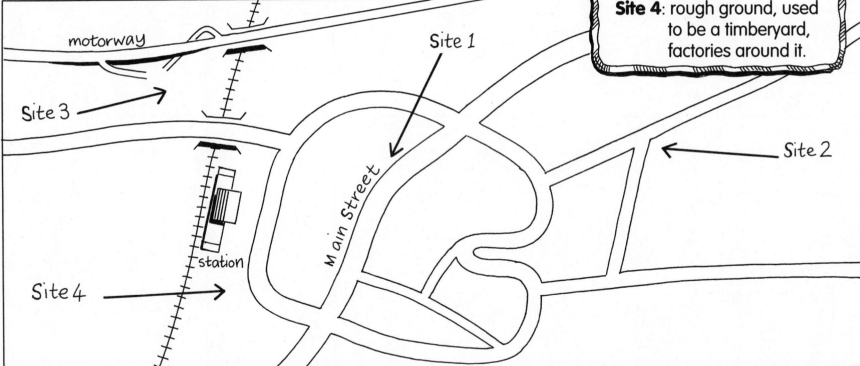

Geography

People who help us

There are lots of people who help us.
♣ Look at the picture. Which services are being used and what are the people doing?

♣ On the back of this sheet, write a list of things to do in an emergency, starting with: Dial 999....

Name _____

Problems of quarrying

Problems of quarrying

❖ Look at the picture below on the left. It shows some of the problems caused by quarrying.
❖ Mark with a cross all the problems you can see in the picture. Then list them on the back of this sheet.
❖ Next to each problem in your list write how you think it has been solved in the second picture below on the right.

Opencast coal-mining

Some people work in coal-mines. If the coal is near the surface it is mined by digging a large hole. This is called opencast coal-mining.
❖ Use the words in the box opposite to fill in the labels on the pictures.
❖ Explain how the coal is taken from the ground to the surface.

truck	coal
trees	fields
excavator	farm
heap of waste	

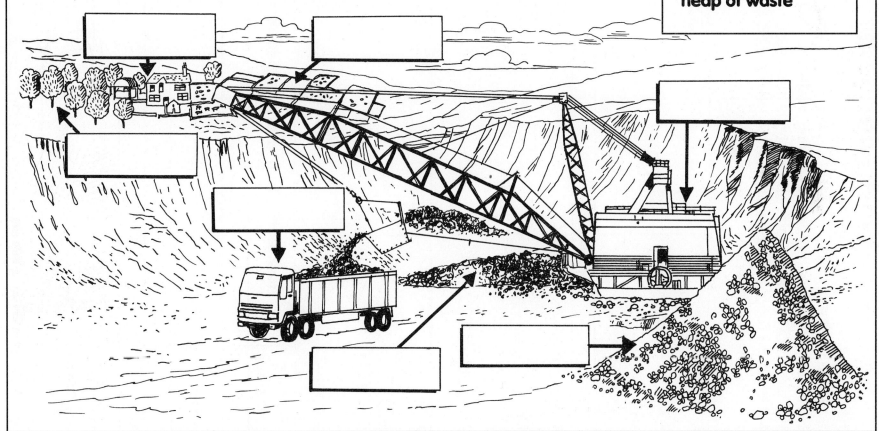

Name _____

Work dangers

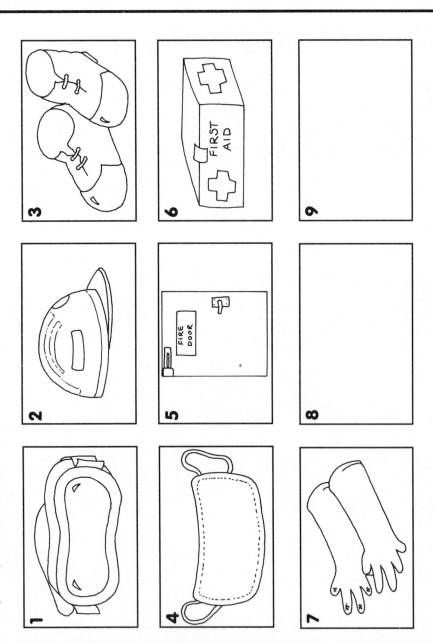

Work dangers

Work can be dangerous.

♣ Look at the numbered pictures below. Write each number in the table and alongside say how each item protects people at work.

♣ Draw two more examples of protective items. Add them to the table and say why they are needed.

Picture number	How each item protects people							

56

Name _____

What kind of work?

What kind of work?

♣ Look at the pictures below, read the instructions and then complete the graphs.
• If the picture shows a person making something colour one box in A.
• If the picture shows a person digging colour one box in B.
• If the picture shows a person helping colour in one box in C.
• Label each picture A, B or C in the small box.

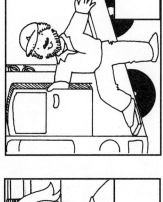
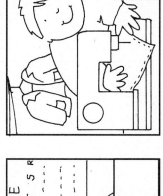

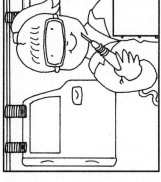

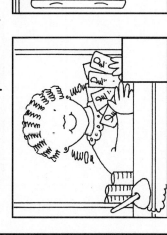
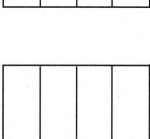

C = helping

B = digging

A = making

♣ Carry out a class survey of the jobs your parents do and draw graphs similar to A, B and C. Do more parents work as makers, diggers or helpers?

Name _____

An industrial estate

An industrial estate

Below is a map of an industrial estate. The companies can be sorted into three groups; cars, food and others.

❖ For each company, colour in one square in the correct part of the graph to show which group it is in.

• How many firms are there in each group? _____

• Which is the biggest group? _____

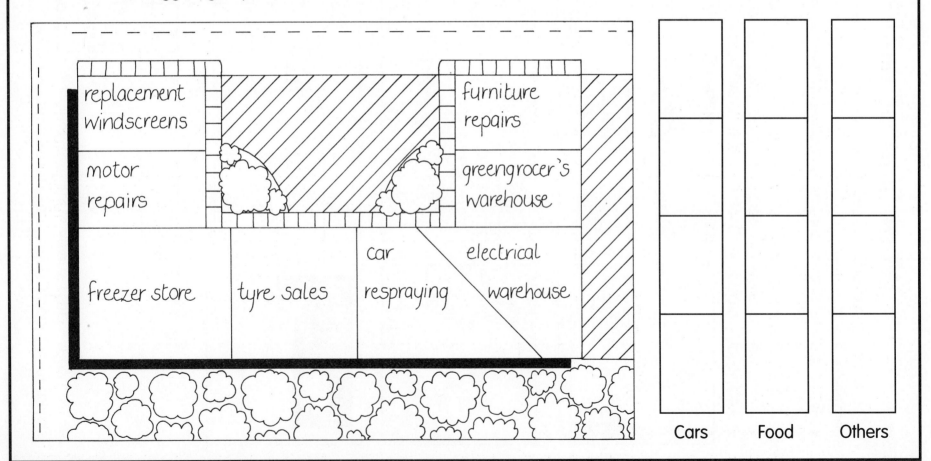

Name _____

Materials in cars

❖ Use the key to colour in the different parts of the car in the picture below.

steel bodywork	**-**	**green**
glass windows	**-**	**yellow**
plastic seats	**-**	**brown**
rubber tyres	**-**	**black**
aluminium wheels	**-**	**red**

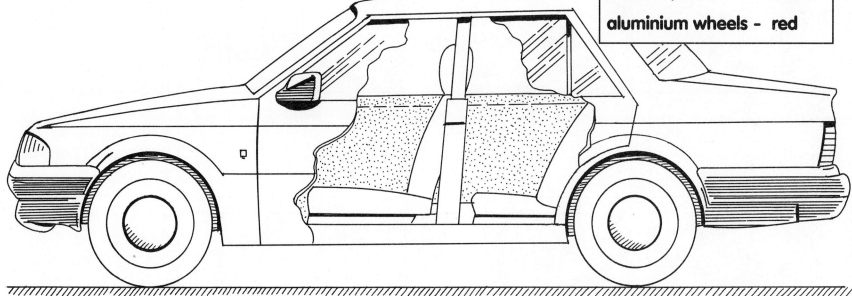

❖ Find out the answers to the following questions. Write your answers on the back of this sheet.

• Which parts of a car wear out first?

• How could this be slowed down?

• How could parts of cars be used again?

Name _____

Making cars

Making cars

The car industry is an assembly industry. This means that workers put components (parts) together.
❖ Write the correct sentence from the list under each diagram.
❖ Cut out the pictures with their labels and arrange them in a flow diagram to show
how a car is assembled from start to finish.

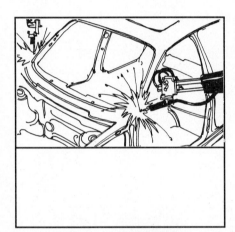

- This car is being painted by a robot.

- The engine is being lowered into the car.

- This person is assembling parts of the engine.

- The car is being driven off the assembly line.

- This person is fitting instruments on the dashboard.

- They are welding the car body.

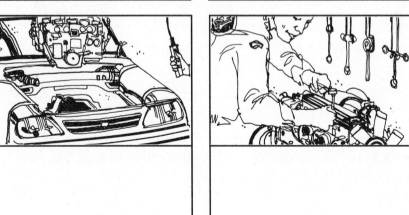

Geography

Finding the best place: 1

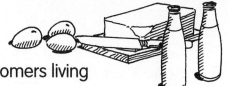

On the map of the village below, a farmer has a dairy at A. She sells milk to all the customers living in the houses shown in the village.

    She wants to open a shop to sell other dairy produce as well. People from all the houses will visit the shop.

✤ Look at the map and decide whether she should choose postion B, C or D for her shop. Explain why you chose that particular site.

✤ Do other people in the class agree with your choice of site?

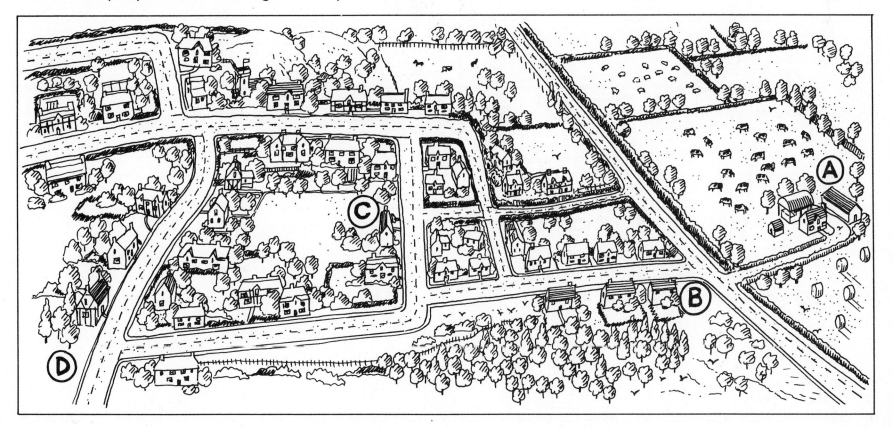

Name _____

Finding the best place: 2

This map shows a small market town. There are three busy roads leaving the town that are linked by the ring road. There are two garages selling petrol.

♣ The Longon Oil Company wants to build a third petrol station. Which of the sites numbered 1 to 4 would you recommend? Why? Write your reasons on the back of this sheet.

♣ A new housing estate is being built. Waitley Foods want to build a supermarket in the area. Which of the sites A to D would you recommend? Why? Write your reasons on the back of this sheet.

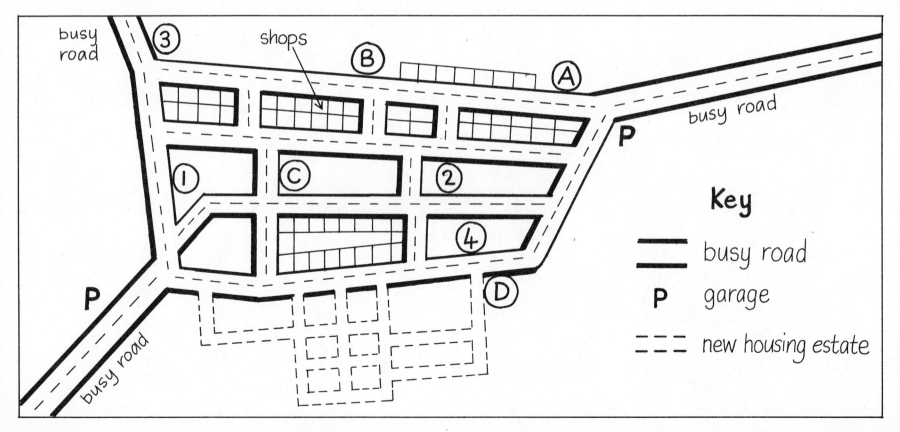

In the park

♣ Look at these people in the park.
♣ Colour in red the people who are playing.
♣ Colour in green the people who are working.

Seaside

Name _____

Seaside

❖ Look at this picture of a seaside place in summer. Colour it in like this:

- hotels – red;
- ice-cream stall – green;
- beach – yellow;
- yacht – brown;
- pleasure boat – black;
- promenade – orange.

❖ Label the pier.

Geography

Name _____

Postcard from the coast

Imagine you are on holiday. The postcard below shows a picture of the area where you are staying.
❧ On the back of the postcard, also shown below, write the name and address of the person sitting next to you.
❧ Then describe what you have been doing on your holiday and what you have seen.

Dear

ADDRESS

_____

_____

_____

_____

_____

Name _____

Mapping the park

Mapping the park

Here is a map of a park.

❧ Colour the lake in blue.
❧ Colour the paths in brown.
❧ Colour the trees in green.
❧ Colour the flower beds in yellow.
❧ Colour the buildings in black.

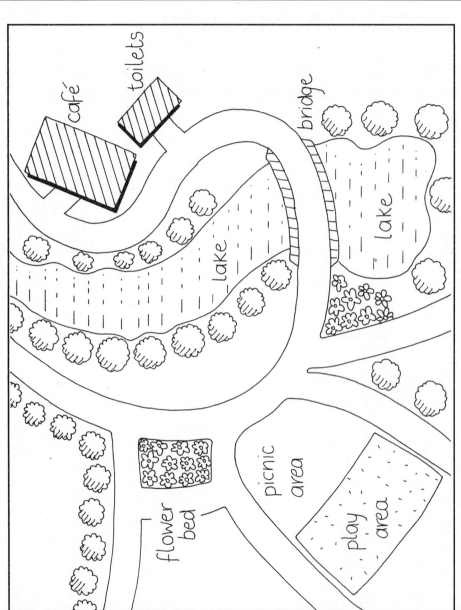

café

toilets

bridge

lake

lake

flower bed

picnic area

play area

❧ Draw a key to show what the colours mean.

❧ Draw a red line to show the route from the play area to the café.

Geography

Winter in the mountains

- ❖ Look at the Alpine scene below.
- ❖ Label these things on the picture: hotel, trees, chair-lift, lake, car park, ski-tow.
- ❖ Colour in red the people who are skiing, in green the people who are skating and in yellow the people who are sledging.

Summer in the mountains

Summer in the mountains

This picture shows a scene in the mountains in summer.

♣ List all the sports you can see people playing.
♣ Mark with a cross all the things that would be different if this picture showed a winter scene.

Name _____

Spare time

♣ Carry out a survey of how you and your friends spend your spare time.

♣ To help you, fill in the leisure diary below for a week. Each day record your spare time activities and how much time you spend doing them.

Day	am	pm
Monday		
Tuesday		
Wednesday		
Thursday		
Friday		
Saturday		
Sunday		

♣ How many different things do you do in your leisure time?

Using the park

This is a picture of a park in a town. People have different ideas about how a park should be used.
❖ On the back of this sheet, write what you think each of the groups of people numbered 1–5 might be saying about the things they can see and hear.

Name _____

Coastline

The map below shows part of a coastline.

✤ Decide where would be the best place to site each of the following features and use symbols to mark them on the map.

● **Power station**: needs flat land for the cooling towers and lots of water nearby for cooling process. It should not be positioned too near the resort but quite close to the town.

● **Pier**: needs to be near the beach and the resort.

● **Marina**: needs to be near the resort.

● **Lighthouse**: needs to be on the point of the coastline furthest out into the sea so that ships can see it.

● **Coastguard station**: needs to be on a high point so that the coastguards can see as much of the coast as possible.

● **Pipeline**: needs to be as far from the resort as possible, to take sewage from the town out to sea.

✤ Draw a key to show what your symbols mean.

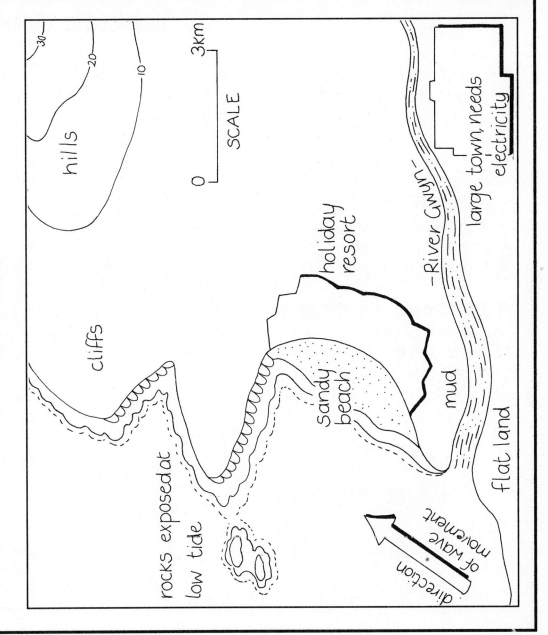

hills

30
20
10

SCALE

0   3km

cliffs

holiday resort

River Gwyn

large town, needs electricity

mud

sandy beach

rocks exposed at low tide

flat land

direction of wave movement

Name _____

Time outdoors

This map shows an area where there are lots of different ways to spend your spare time.

✤ Plan the following four trips from the city:
• for half a day in summer;
• for half a day in winter;
• for a week in winter;
• for a week in summer.

✤ For each trip, describe where you would go and give reasons for your choice. Explain how you would get there, how far you would have to travel and where you might stay.

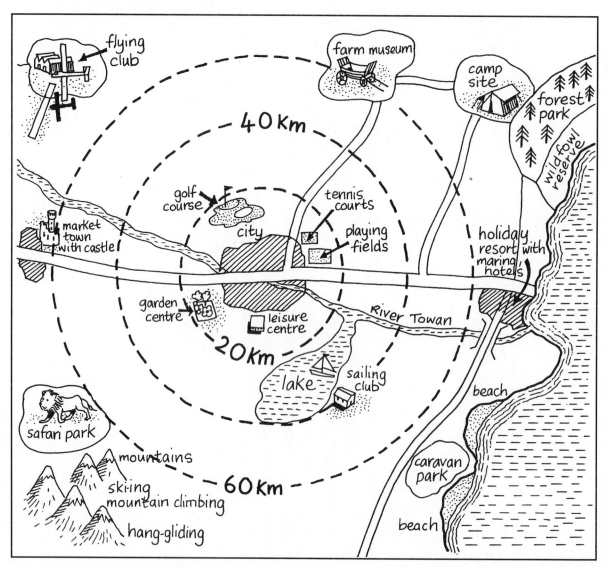

Time outdoors

Geography

Name _____

Road signs

❖ Look at these road signs.
❖ Colour the edges in red and the pictures
  in the middles in black.
❖ Write the correct label under each sign
  using the words in the box opposite.

| roundabout |
| cycle route |
| bridge |
| children |

Vehicles and drivers

Vehicles and drivers

❖ Draw lines to match each driver with the right vehicle.

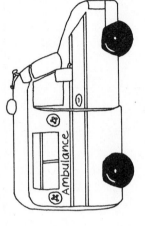 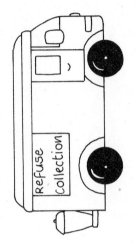 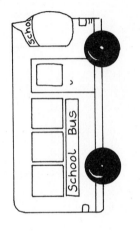 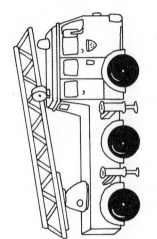 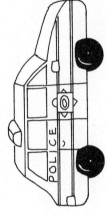

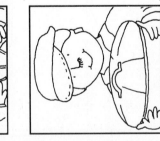  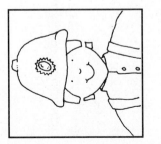

❖ On the back of this sheet, draw another vehicle and its driver.

Name _____

Today they saw on the road...

The picture below shows what these children saw on the road today.
Lucy saw a bus.

❖ What did Scott see? _____

❖ What did Mehmuda see? _____

❖ What did Peter see? _____

❖ What did Emily see? _____

Geography

75

Name _____

Today they heard on the road ...

The picture below shows what these children heard on the road today.
Scott heard a police car.

❖ What did Lucy hear? _____

❖ What did Mehmuda hear? _____

❖ What did Peter hear? _____

❖ What did Emily hear? _____

Geography

Name _____

On the move

The picture below shows different types of transport. Some travel quickly, others travel more slowly.

❖ Colour in green the two fastest types of transport.

❖ Colour in red the two slowest types of transport.

Some types of transport are used to carry big, heavy loads. Others carry only light loads.

❖ Write down the best type of transport for each of the following:

• a letter from Britain to Canada _____

• timber from a forest to a sawmill _____

• oil from Venezuela to Britain _____

• coal from a mine to a power-station _____

Name _____

How far?

Equipment and supplies for the three mines near Cache Creek are brought by ship to the landing stage.

❖ Look at the map. There is a straight line scale. The kilometres have been marked on the road using the scale.

❖ Measure the following distances.
• How far is it from the landing stage to Mine A by road? ☐ km

• How far is it from the landing stage to Mine C by road? ☐ km

• How far is it from the landing stage to Mine C in a straight line? ☐ km

• How far is it from the landing stage to Mine B in a straight line? ☐ km

• How far is it from the landing stage to Mine B by road? ☐ km

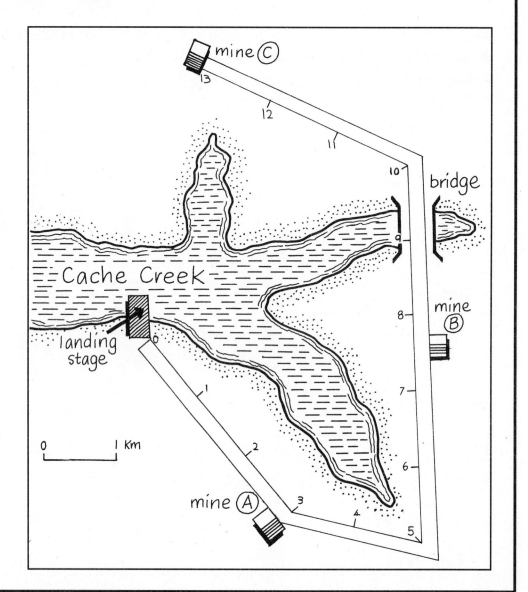

How far?

Name _____

Motorway journeys

✤ Look at the map.
✤ Fill in the table showing which motorways you would use for each journey. The first one has been done for you.

Journey	Motorways
Exeter to London	M5, M4
Southampton to Birmingham	
London to Hull	
Liverpool to Carlisle	
Manchester to Swansea	
Cambridge to Dover	
Edinburgh to Glasgow	

Name _____

Journeys between North and South America

Journeys between North and South America

✤ Look at the map. It shows some big ports in North and South America. It also shows the Panama Canal.

♣ Draw different coloured lines to show each of the journeys listed in the table below.

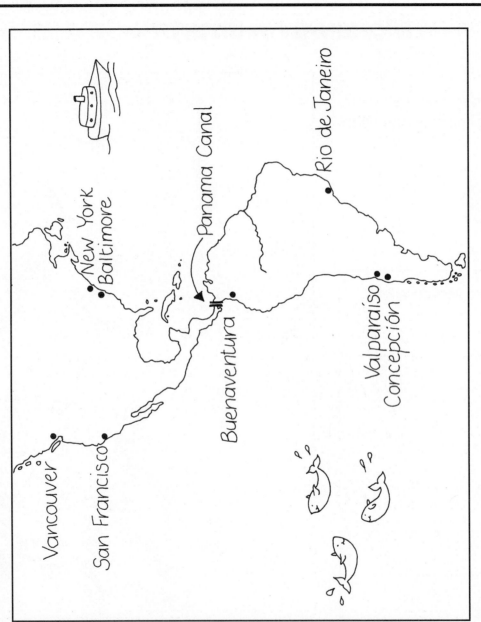

✤ Use an atlas to complete this table. The first one has been done for you.

From	In country	To	In country	Uses Panama Canal?
Valparaíso	Chile	Baltimore	USA	yes
Rio de Janeiro		Vancouver		
San Francisco		Concepción		
Buenaventura		New York		

Geography

Journeys through the Channel Tunnel

♣ Look at this diagram. It shows the likely travelling times between some major European cities, once the Channel Tunnel is in use.

♣ How long will the journey take:

• from London to Brussels?

_____

• from Birmingham to Paris?

_____

• from Edinburgh to Milan?

_____

• from Leeds to Rome?

_____

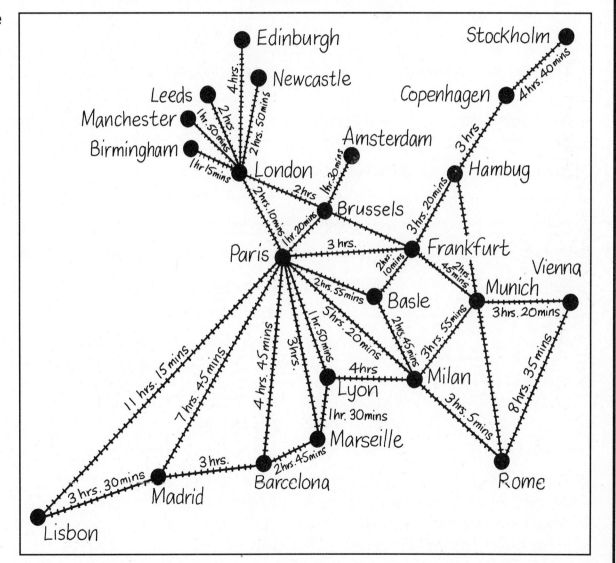

Name _____

Getting around town

The chart below lists some of the advantages and disadvantages of using different types of transport in towns.
♣ Complete the chart by including factors such as safety, luggage space, distance, waiting time and comfort.

Transport type	Time/cost factors	Other factors
Train	Expensive but fast	
Car	Expensive but can be slow	
Bus	Fairly cheap but can be slow	
Motorcycle	Fast and quite cheap	
Underground	Fast and quite cheap but only goes to some parts of the city	

♣ Discuss which method of transport might be best for:
• Mr Aziz who has to travel 2km each way to go to work every day across a busy town;
• Mrs Lowe who lives 30 km from the city, but has to go to work there three days each week;
• a rapid express delivery service in the town.

Name _____

Moving goods

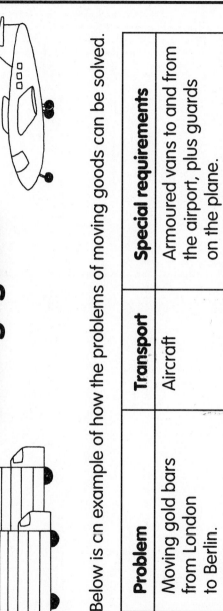

Below is an example of how the problems of moving goods can be solved.

Problem	Transport	Special requirements
Moving gold bars from London to Berlin.	Aircraft	Armoured vans to and from the airport, plus guards on the plane.

✤ Now solve these transport problems.

Problem	Transport	Special requirements
Moving strawberries from southern Spain to Manchester.		
Moving large parts of an oil rig from Newcastle to Aberdeen.		
Moving two million tonnes of oil from Venezuela to London.		
Putting a weather satellite in orbit over the equator.		

Placing signs

Placing signs

✤ Look at these road signs.
♣ Write underneath each sign what it means.

1

2

3
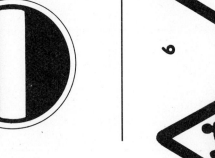

4

5

6

7

✤ Using the numbers, mark on the map below some of the places where each sign should be located.
♣ Add the positions of some other signs to the map and draw them on the back of this sheet.

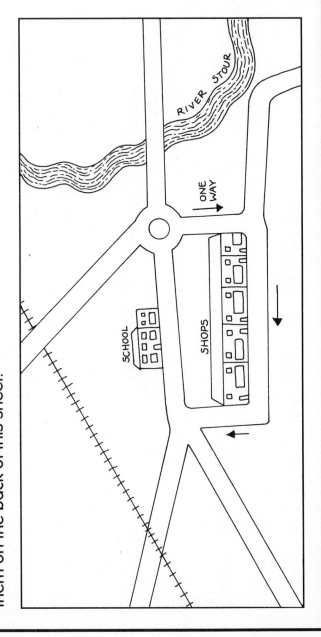

Name _____

Milk round

Mr Page has to deliver milk to all the houses shown by a dot on the map below.

♣ Draw a line with arrows to show the best route he can take.

♣ How far does he have to travel using your route.

♣ How does your route compare with those drawn by others in the class?

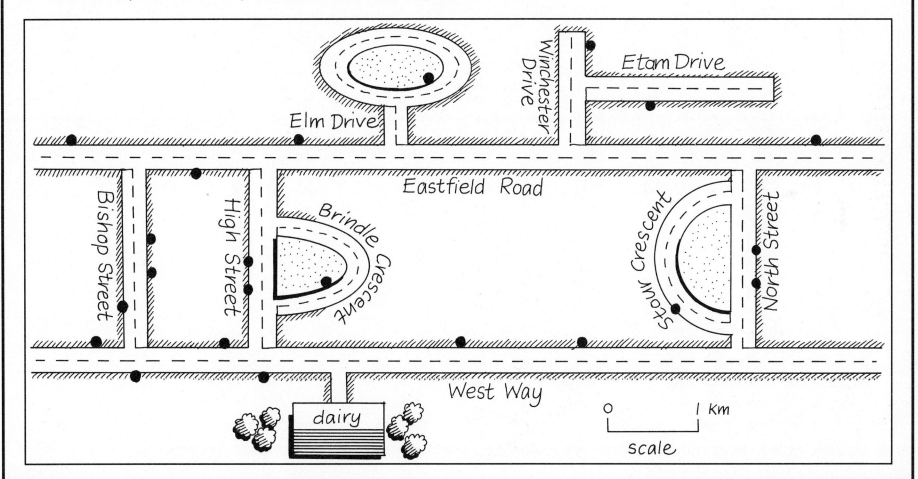

Building a motorway

Name _____

Building a motorway

✤ Look at the map below and plan a route for the M99 to join up the two existing sections. Note the following points to guide your planning:
- the route must not cost more than 300 units (see table opposite);
- the mountains of Eagle Crag are too steep to build the road on;
- the route should disrupt as few people's homes as possible.

Work	Cost
To build 1km of road	20 units
To cross over marshland	40 units
To build a bridge	20 units
To cut down trees	20 units
To demolish a house	40 units
To buy land from The Grange	40 units
Total cost of building my route	units

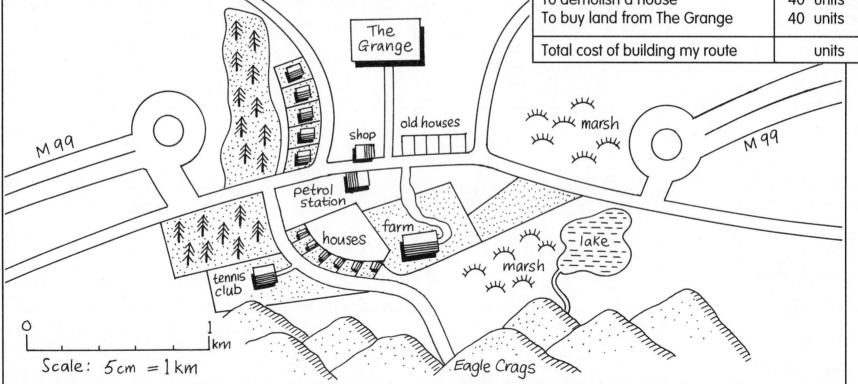

Scale: 5cm = 1km

✤ Use the table to work out how much your route will cost to build and then draw it on to the map.

Name _____

Motorway debate

These local people are interested in the motorway route you have planned.

We don't want the motorway near our houses.

Joan Armstrong
Residents' Association

I am in danger of losing my passing trade.

John Evans
Garage owner

I want a route that is as straight as possible and no more delays in the village.

Lucy Walker
Lorry driver

Keep it away from my house and my land.

George Heath
Owner of The Grange

Keep it away from the tennis club. We don't have another site.

Sarah Smith
Tennis Club President

❖ Fill in the first part of the table below to say whether or not you think each person would vote for your route. Put a ✓ for **yes** and a ✗ for **no**. Complete the table by saying why you think each person should vote for your route.

Person	Their vote	Why they should vote for your route
Joan Armstrong		
John Evans		
Lucy Walker		
George Heath		
Sarah Smith		

Weather changes

Name _____

Weather changes

❖ What type of weather is shown in each of the pictures below?

❖ Use the words from the box opposite to label each weather picture.

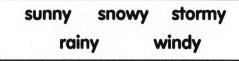

| sunny | snowy | stormy |
| rainy | | windy |

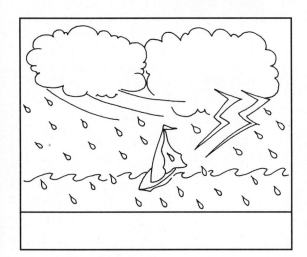

❖ Draw your own pictures in the empty boxes and label them to show:

- a snowy day;
- a windy day.

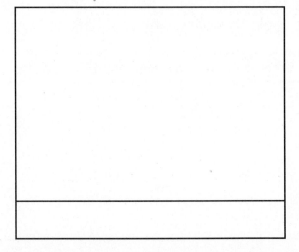

Name _____

A week's weather

The chart below shows what the weather was like in one week.

Key				
windy	cloudy	lightning	sunny	rain

Day	Morning	Afternoon
Monday	windy	cloudy
Tuesday	sunny	cloudy/rain
Wednesday	windy/lightning	windy/sunny
Thursday	sunny	sunny
Friday	windy	cloudy/lightning

❖ What was the weather like on Monday morning? _____

❖ What was the weather like on Wednesday morning? _____

❖ What was the weather like all day Thursday? _____

❖ How many days had lightning? _____

❖ Which were the best days for sunbathing? _____

Name _____

This week's weather

This week's weather

❖ Record the weather each day for a week on this chart using symbols.

Date on Day 1:	Morning		Afternoon	
	Before play	After play	Before play	After play
Day 1				
Day 2				
Day 3				
Day 4				
Day 5				

❖ Below, draw a key for the symbols you have used on the chart.

Key

Name _____

Danger from the weather

♣ Look at the chart below.
• What was the weather like on Wednesday?   • On how many days did it rain?

_____   _____

Monday	**Tuesday**	**Wednesday**	**Thursday**	**Friday**
windy	rain	foggy	sunny	cloudy

♣ Under each of these pictures write the day of the week when the event happened.

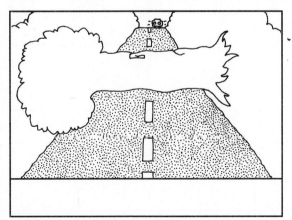   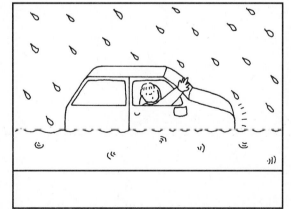   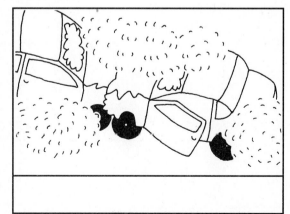

Different weather

Different weather

❖ Look at the pictures below.
❖ Write the words in the box in the correct places on the pictures below.

cloud	**lightning**
rain	**snow**

There are some clues in the pictures which tell us that they show windy days.
❖ Write **wind** next to each clue that you spot.

Name _____

The right clothes

✤ In what weather would you wear each of these items of clothing?
Draw a suitable weather symbol in the box below each item of clothing.
✤ Draw a key for your symbols on the back of the sheet.

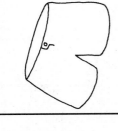
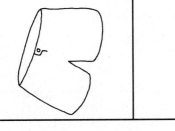
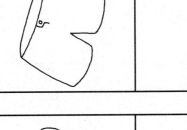
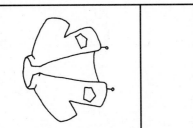
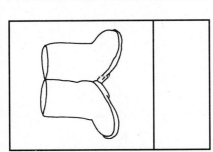
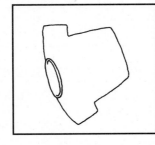
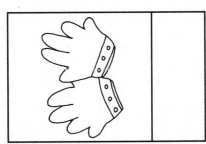
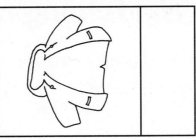

✤ List the clothes shown above under the correct heading in the table below.

Only useful in one type of weather	Useful in many types of weather

Wind strength

Name _____

Wind strength

Each picture below shows how winds of different strengths can affect people.

❖ Put the right label from the list opposite under each picture.

❖ In the empty box, draw a picture to match the remaining label.

calm	storm
light breeze	gale

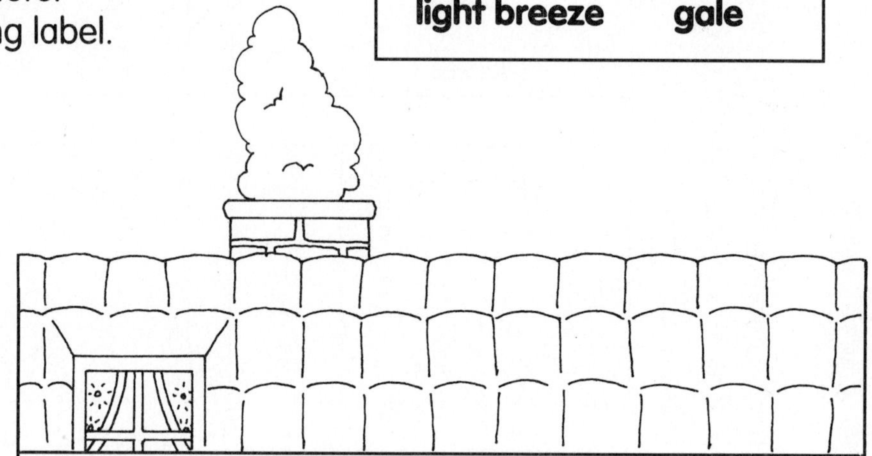

Geography

Recording the weather: rainfall

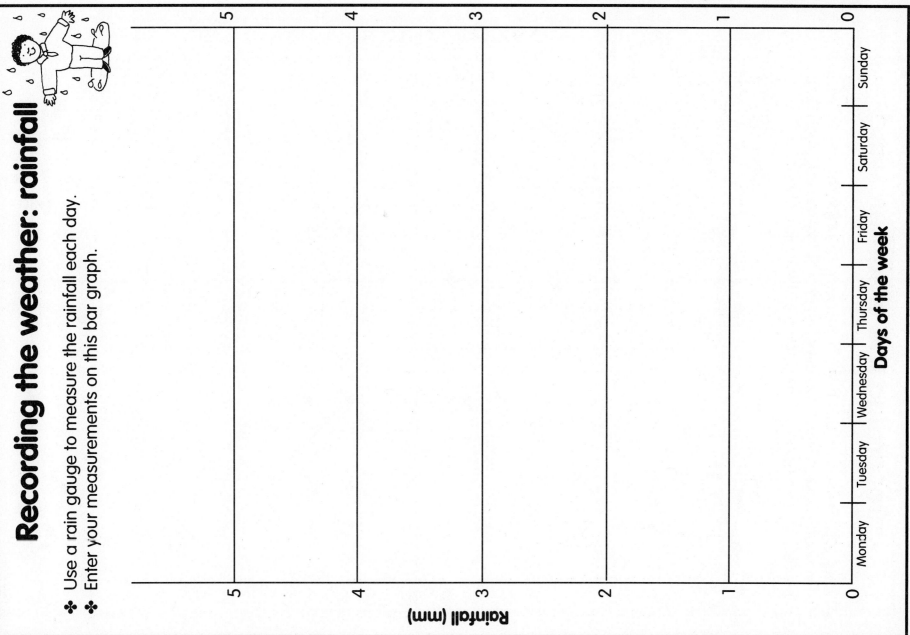

Recording the weather: rainfall

♣ Use a rain gauge to measure the rainfall each day.
♣ Enter your measurements on this bar graph.

Rainfall (mm)

5   4   3   2   1   0

Monday   Tuesday   Wednesday   Thursday   Friday   Saturday   Sunday

Days of the week

Name _____

Recording the weather: wind

Recording the weather: wind

A wind-rose is used to record the direction from which the wind blows.
♣ Every day observe the wind direction and fill in one square on the wind-rose below. From which direction did the wind blow most?

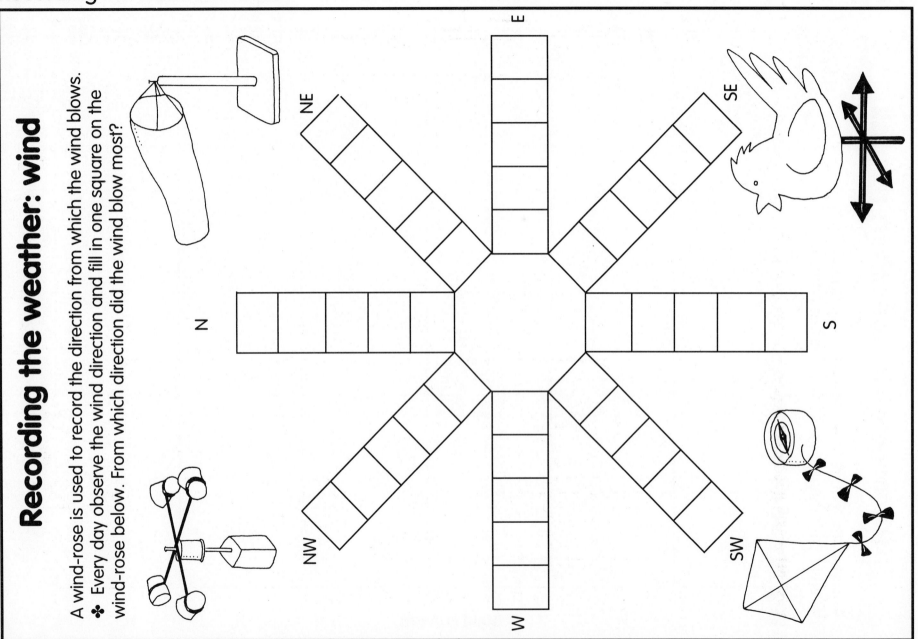

Geography

Recording the weather: temperature

Recording the weather: temperature

♣ Measure the outside temperature with a thermometer every day at the same time, for example 9 am. Enter your results on this graph.

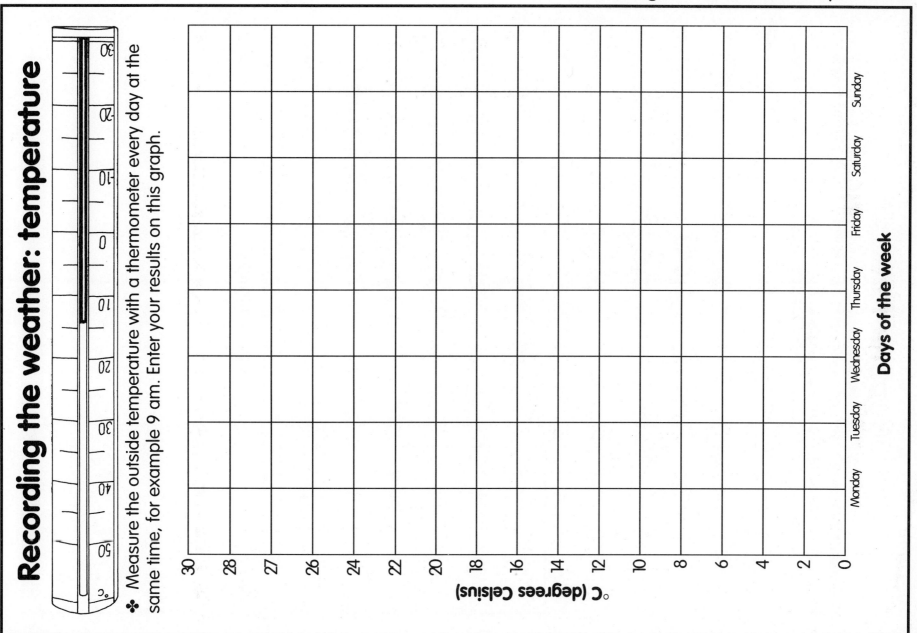

°C (degrees Celsius)

30
28
27
26
24
22
20
18
16
14
12
10
8
6
4
2
0

Monday   Tuesday   Wednesday   Thursday   Friday   Saturday   Sunday

Days of the week

Weather forecast

Weather forecast

♣ Look at this winter weather forecast map. Fill in the table below to say what type of weather each area is going to have.

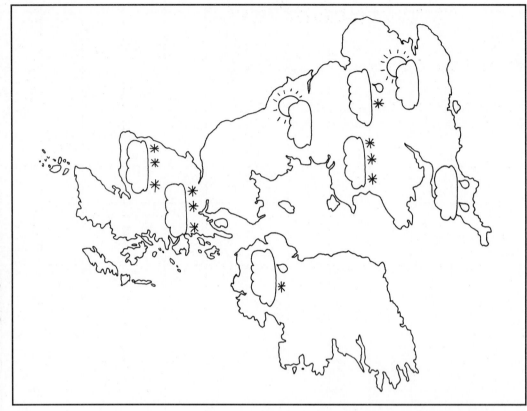

KEY		
		snow
		rain
		cloudy
		sunny intervals
		sleet

Area	Weather forecast
South-west England	
South-east England	
Midlands	
Wales	
Northern England	
Scotland	
Northern Ireland	

Name _____

Problem weather

People all over the world are affected by changes in the weather.

❖ Fill in the table to show how the weather can create problems for people and animals. The first one has been done for you.

Activity	Weather	Typical part of the world affected	Possible problems
Feeding sheep	Heavy snow	Scotland	Sheep buried or cut off without food
Fishing	High winds		
Mountain climbing	Rain		
Plane journey	Fog		
Playing tennis	Sleet		
Harvesting wheat	Thunderstorm's		
Picking bananas	Hurricane		
Growing cherries	Frost		

Name _____

Cloud types

The pictures below show four different types of cloud and the heights at which they are found.

Cirrus: thin, high whispy clouds

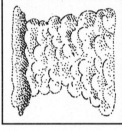

Cumulus: white, fluffy clouds

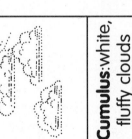

Cumulo-nimbus: thunder clouds

Stratus: thick layers of cloud

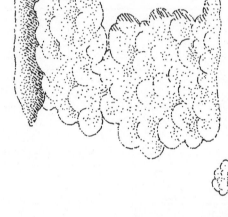

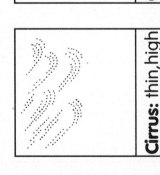

Airport

Height (thousand metres)

10 8 6 4 2 0

✿ Complete the table by listing the clouds that a jet might pass through at each stage of its flight up to 10,000 metres, from lowest to highest.

Height (metres)	Clouds
2,000	
4,000	
6,000	
8,000	
10,000	

Geography

Weathering

Weathering is the wearing away of rock by sun, frost, rain and plants. The picture below shows weathering taking place in a valley. There are different types of weathering.

1 Biological weathering: plant roots prise open cracks in the rock.

2 Mechanical weathering: the rock surface becomes hot, expands and cracks.

3 Chemical weathering: rainwater dissolves rocks.

4 Freeze thaw weathering: when rainwater freezes in joints at night, it expands, cracking the joints.

❖ Number the four circle pictures to say which type of weathering each one shows.
On the back of this sheet explain your choices.

Water cycle

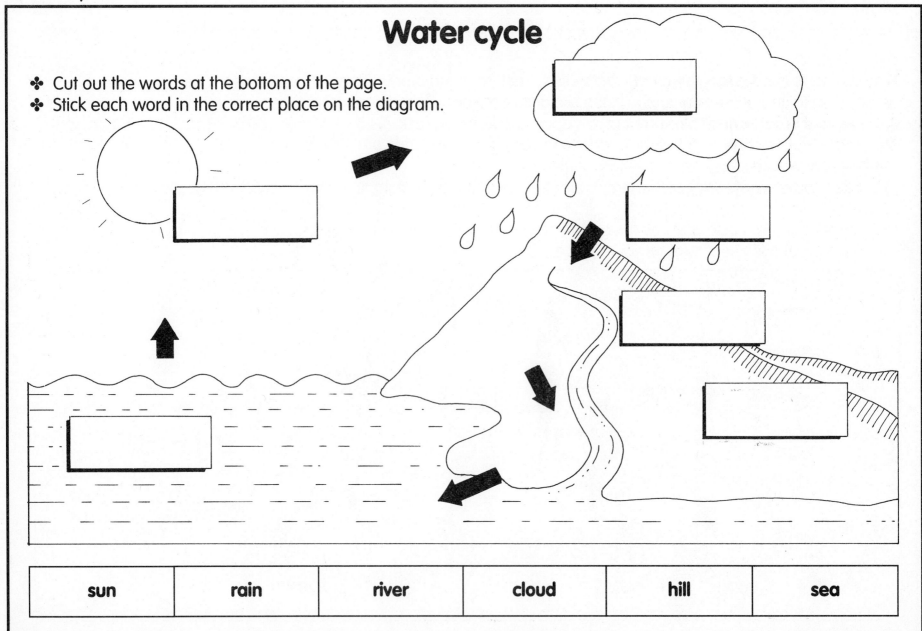

Water cycle

❖ Cut out the words at the bottom of the page.
❖ Stick each word in the correct place on the diagram.

sun	rain	river	cloud	hill	sea

Name _____

Living on an island

✤ Look at this picture of a group of islands.
✤ Choose the right word from the list below to write in each empty label on the picture.

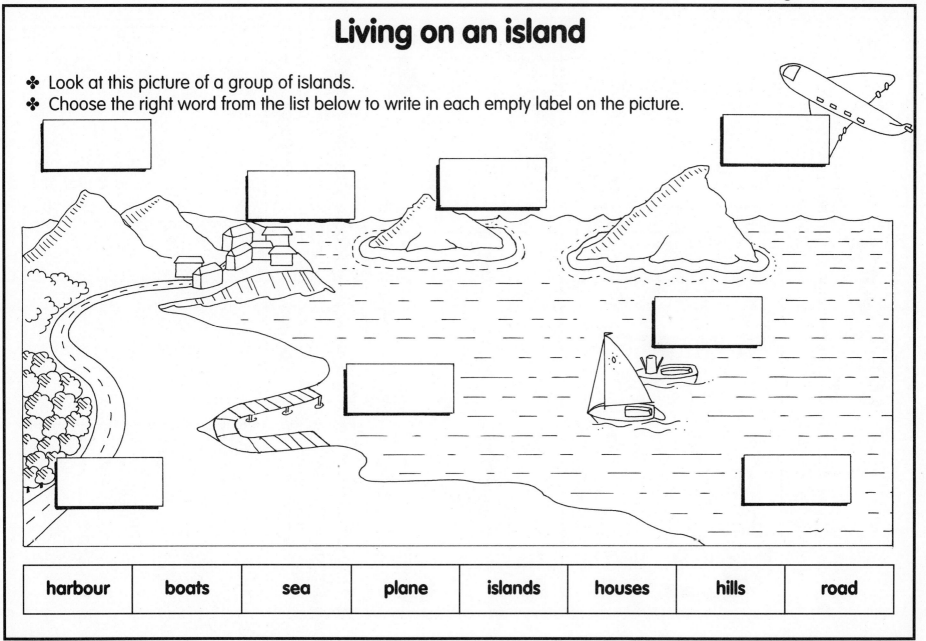

| harbour | boats | sea | plane | islands | houses | hills | road |

Name _____

Using water in Britain

Using water

❖ Look at these pictures. Say what is happening in each one and how water is being used.

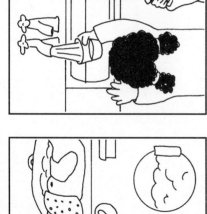

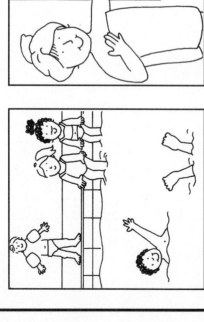

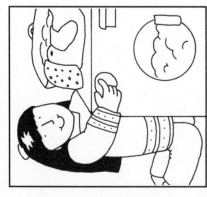

❖ Now write each of the uses of water shown above under one of the headings in the table.

For fun	For work	For health

104

Name _____

Water around us

❧ Fill in the labels under the pictures below using the words in this box:

water meter	drain	fire hydrant	foul sewer

❧ On the line under each label, write whether the picture suggests water being brought **into** the area or being **taken away**.

❧ Carry out a survey of water signs and covers around your school. Count how many of each type you can find and mark their position on a simple plan.

Name _____

Keeping water out

✤ Look at this picture of a house. Put the right letter by each label in the table below.
✤ Also on the table, write a sentence explaining how each labelled part keeps water
out of the house.

Letter	Object	How it keeps the water out
	downpipe	
	bricks	
	glass	
	tiled roof	
	canopy	

✤ On the back of this sheet, draw a simple picture of your school. Show the different parts which keep water out.
Write down how water is kept out by each part.

Geography

Name _____

The world's rivers

The chart below shows the length of some of the world's rivers.
❧ Shade in the length of each river on the measurement graph.

River	Length (km)	0	500	1,000	1,500	2,000	2,500	3,000	3,500	4,000	4,500	5,000	6,000	6,500
Rhine	1,300													
Nile	6,700													
Amazon	6,500													
Mississippi	6,000													
Yangtze	5,000													
Amur	4,400													
MacKenzie	4,300													

❧ Mark these rivers on the blank world map.

Geography

107

Uses of the river

Name _____

Uses of the river

The picture below shows how people like to spend their spare time on the river.

♣ What different river activities you can see?

♣ Sort the activities into the following groups:
- noisy/quiet;
- dangerous/safe;
- active/relaxed;
- in water/on water/near water.

✱ Which activities are likely to:
- pollute the water;
- damage the river banks;
- affect wildlife?

Name _____

From source to sea

The diagram below shows the course of a river from the hills to the sea.

✤ Fill in the labels on the diagram using the words in the box at the bottom of the page.

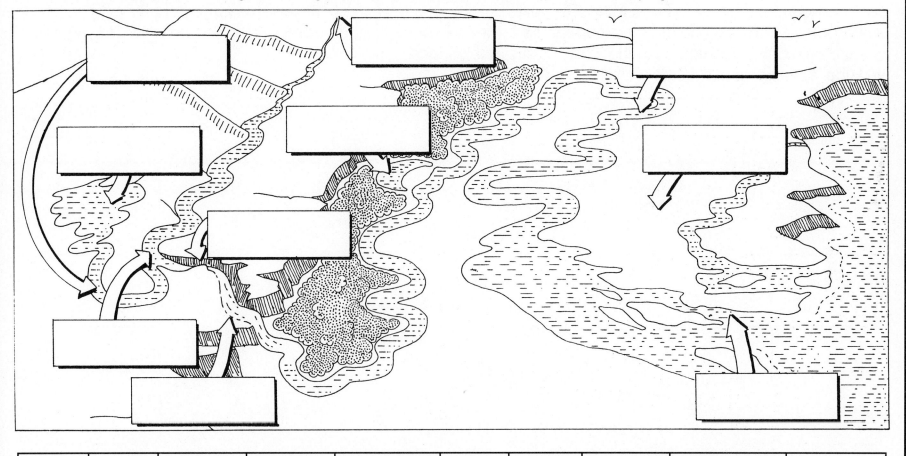

| delta | gorge | tributary | meander | flood plain | lake | source | waterfall | ox-bow lake | confluence |

Name _____

River at work

River at work

The diagram below shows a stream at work in a hilly area. The river works in a **channel**. This is a groove it cuts in the surface. The river picks up pieces of rock, sand and mud and transports them. Rivers are found in valleys. The flat land near the river is the **flood plain**. The valley is surrounded by **steep slopes**. The large pebbles in the river which are not moved along are the **sleeping load**. The smaller pebbles are rolled along as **bed load**. Tiny particles of sand are carried suspended in the water as **suspension load**.

♣ Label the diagram using the words in bold above.

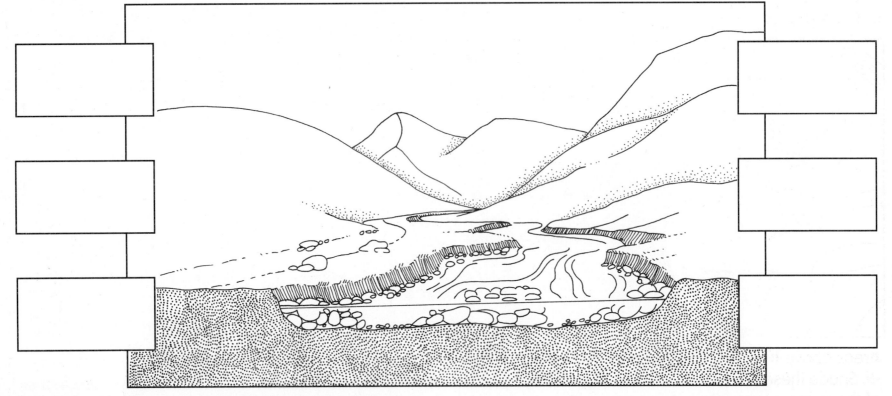

♣ What time of year is shown? How do you know?

Flooding: for and against

It has been proposed to straighten the River Clun to stop it flooding. This would mean strengthening the river banks and dredging a deeper channel.
❖ Look at the map below and the opinions opposite of two local people.
❖ What do you think would be the opinion of:
- a local pub owner in Meanwood whose cellar is regularly flooded;
- a large construction company;
- a conservationist;
- the owner of the caravan site near the river?

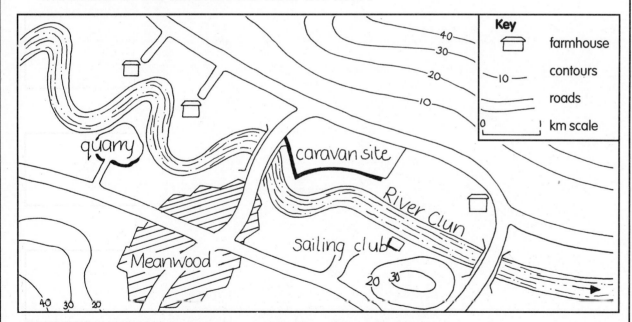

Key
- farmhouse
- contours
- roads
- km scale

Areas above 10 metres are normally free from flooding.
❖ Shade these on the map and mark where the course of the river could be straightened.

What the local people think

Jane Brown
Farmer

'The floods keep my soil fertile. I don't want the flooding to stop.'

Ted Casey
Rescue services

'We have to rescue people and animals at flood time. It is dangerous work. We want the floods stopped.'

The countryside

The countryside

❖ Label this picture using the words in the boxes at the bottom of the page.

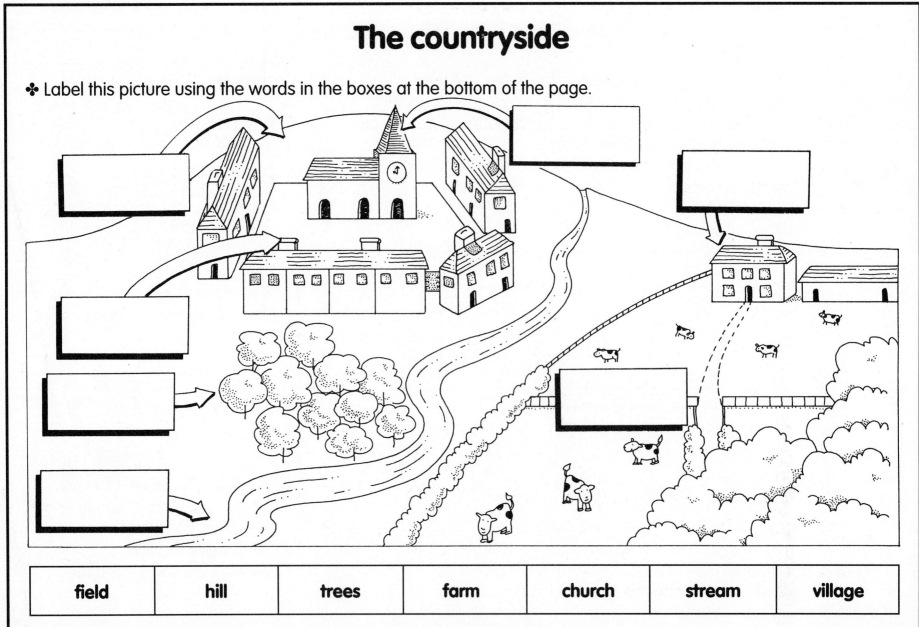

field	hill	trees	farm	church	stream	village

Name _____

Food from the countryside

Food from the countryside

These pictures show some of our foods and where they come from.
♣ Use different coloured lines to join up the pairs of pictures.

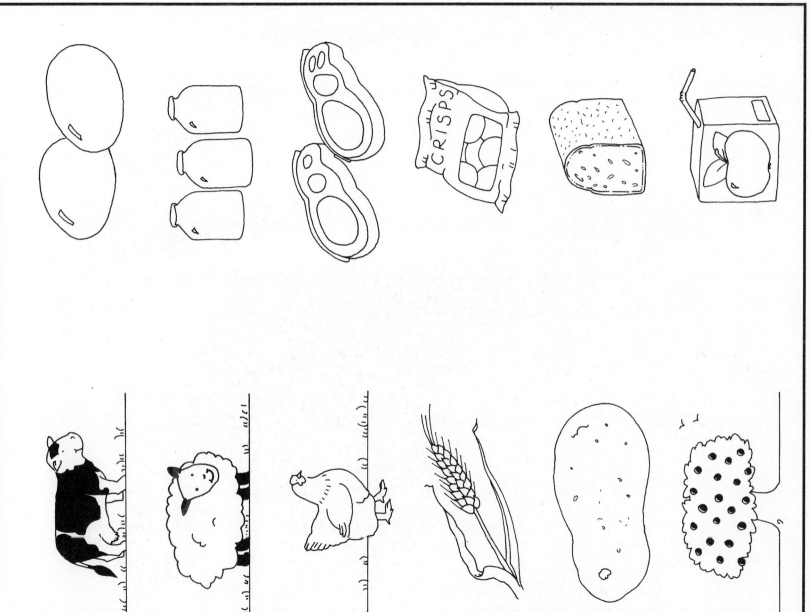

Brooke Farm

Brooke Farm

This is Brooke Farm, near Birmingham.
♣ Colour in the farm using the key.

farmhouse – red	**tractor shed – blue**	**milking shed – yellow**
barn – brown	**orchard – green**	**farmyard – orange**

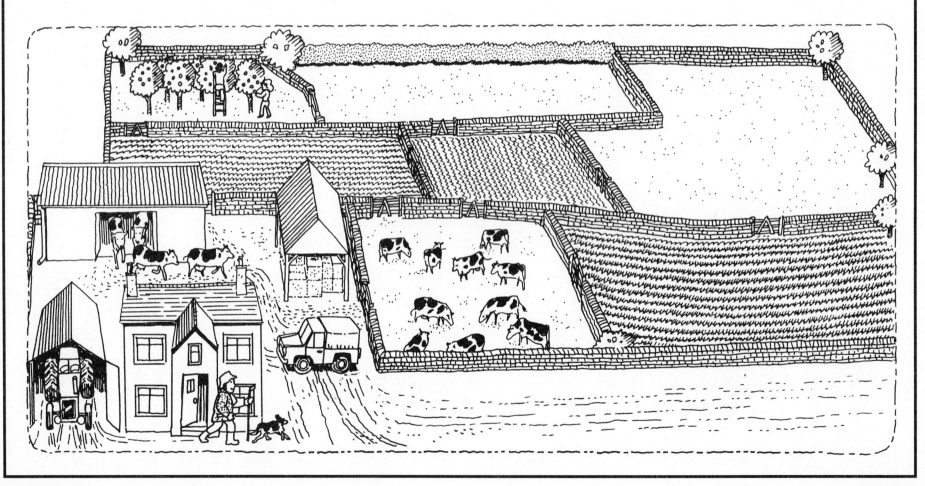

A plan of Brooke Farm

This is a plan of Brooke Farm.
❖ How many fields are there?
❖ How many fields grow grass?

❖ What do you think the other fields are used for?
❖ How many trees are there?

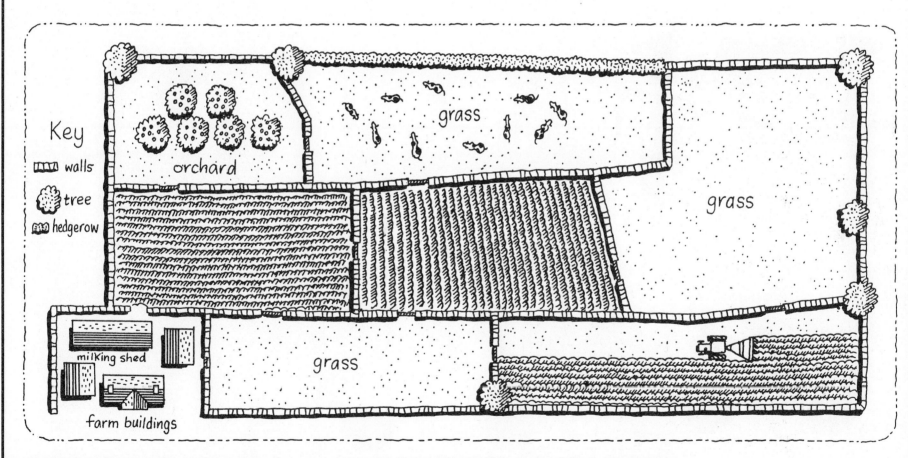

Key

▭▭ walls

🌳 tree

🌿 hedgerow

orchard

grass

grass

grass

milking shed

farm buildings

❖ Draw a line to show the route the cows use to get to the milking shed from their field.

The journey of milk

Name _____

The journey of milk

These pictures show how milk gets from the farm to your home.
✤ Colour in each picture.
✤ In the empty box draw your own picture to show how you might use milk.
✤ Cut out the pictures and arrange them in the right order.

Name _____

Hill farming

Farming in the hills can be hard. Grass is the main crop.
♣ To answer these questions, write the correct field number in each box.

• Which field is the lowest on the hill? ☐   • Which field is being ploughed? ☐

• Which field is the highest on the hill? ☐   • Which is the smallest field? ☐

• In which field are the animals grazing? ☐

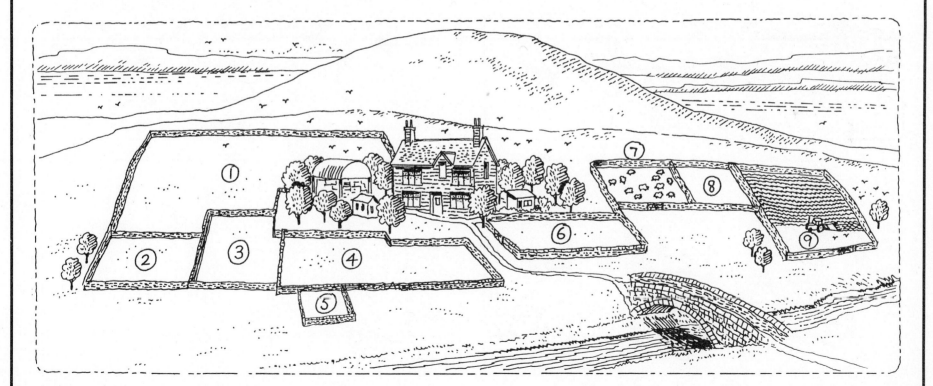

Name _____

Seasonal jobs: 1

Seasonal jobs: 1

There are four seasons; winter, spring, summer and autumn.

These pictures show four jobs that need to be done on a farm at different seasons.
♣ Under each picture write what job is being done and during which season of the year it takes place.

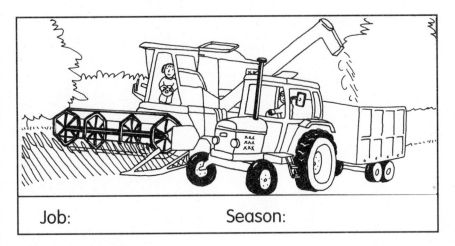

Job: Season:

Job: Season:

Job: Season:

Job: Season:

Seasonal jobs: 2

There are four seasons; winter, spring, summer and autumn.

These pictures show four jobs that need to be done on a farm at different seasons.
♣ Under each picture write what job is being done and during which season of the year it takes place.

Job: Season:

Job: Season:

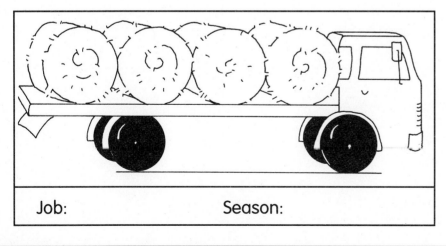

Job: Season:

Job: Season:

Food from other countries

Food from other countries

Our food comes from all over the world.
✤ Look at this greengrocer's display.
✤ Colour in red the foods from Britain.
✤ How many foods come from abroad?
✤ Are more than half the foods grown in Britain?

✤ Collect the labels from tinned fruit and vegetables.
✤ Fill in this list of the foods and the country where each one comes from.

Food	Country of origin

Name _____

Streamside Farm

✤ On this map of Streamside Farm, mark the route a tractor would take from the farmhouse to the Bell Field.

✤ How many fields would the tractor go through?

✤ Count how many fields each crop is growing in. Colour in the right number of squares in the graph for each crop.

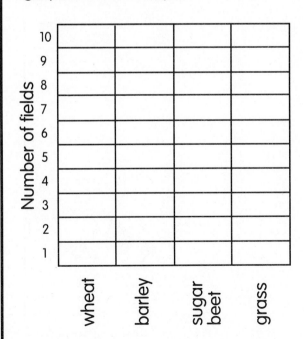

(Graph: Number of fields, scale 1–10, with columns labelled: wheat, barley, sugar beet, grass)

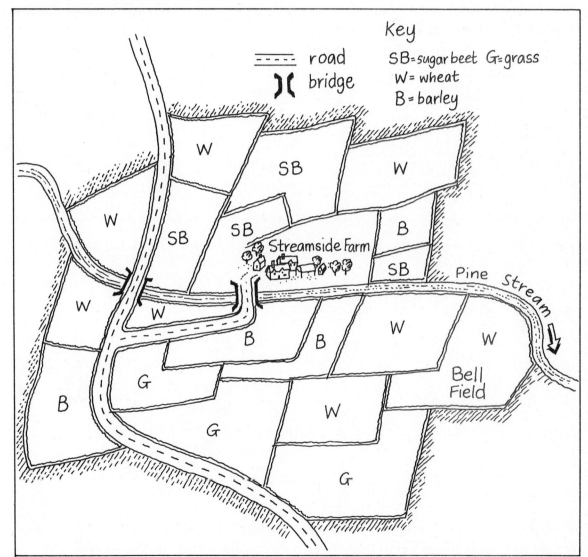

Key
road ====
)(bridge
SB = sugar beet   G = grass
W = wheat
B = barley

Pine Stream

Streamside Farm

Bell Field

Changes in farming

Changes in farming

Farming has changed a lot in the last 100 years. It has also changed the countryside.

❖ Look at these two pictures.

Farming 100 years ago

Farming today

❖ Make a list, on the back of this sheet, of all the changes you can see.

❖ Say why you think these changes may not be good for the wildlife.

Farming decisions

Imagine that this is a picture of your farm.
The table below tells you how often you need to visit each crop in a week.
♣ Decide what crops to grow in fields A, B, C, D and E. Mark your choices on the map.

Crop	Number of visits each crop needs in a week
oats	2
barley	3
grass	1
kitchen garden	8

♣ Now use the table below to decide whether you would keep chickens, which need attention twice each day, in field F, G or H. Mark your decision on the map.

Field	Time taken to walk to field (mins)
F	2
G	4
H	6

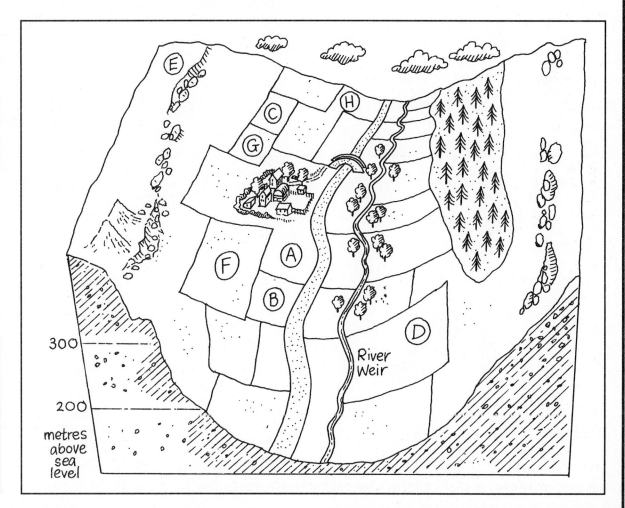

River Weir

300

200

metres above sea level

Spoiling the river

Name _____

Spoiling the river

Rivers are spoiled when people dump rubbish in them. The rubbish is called pollution.

❖ Look at this picture of a river.

❖ Put a cross on all the things that are polluting the river.

❖ Now draw a picture of the river without the pollution.

Geography

Name _____

Improving our environment

Imagine that this is a plan of your playground.
Next to the plan there is a list of things which will improve the playground.
♣ Choose eight things you would like to include in the playground and mark each with a tick in its small box.
♣ Draw each item you have ticked on the plan in the best place.

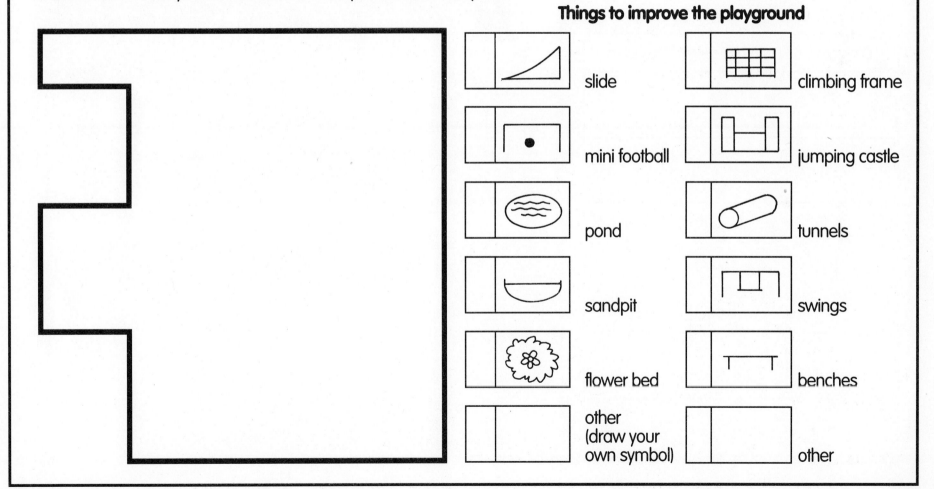

Things to improve the playground

slide

mini football

pond

sandpit

flower bed

other
(draw your
own symbol)

climbing frame

jumping castle

tunnels

swings

benches

other

Name _____

Dangers in the environment

Dangers in the environment

The picture opposite shows some of the dangers in the classroom environment.
♣ Circle six things that are dangerous.
♣ Now list the dangers you have circled and say what might happen.

Danger	What might happen

Using and reusing

Below are some of the things which we use and then throw away.
♣ List each of the items in the picture under one of these headings to show how they might be reused.

New glass	New textiles	New metal	New paper	Hard to reuse

♣ Make a list of things you throw away at school or at home.
♣ Write down how each one could be used again.

Item	How it could be reused

Name _____

Volcano

The diagram below shows a section through a volcano.
♣ Complete the labels using the words in the word bank.

Word bank

**lava flow
magma
volcanic bombs
vent
gas clouds**

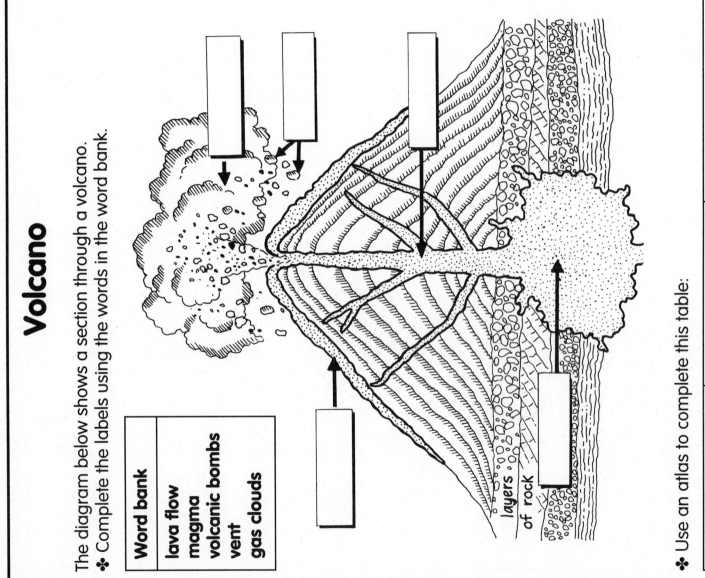

layers
of rock

♣ Use an atlas to complete this table:

Volcano	Country	Latitude and longitude
Mount St Helens		60°N160°E
	Italy	
Cotopaxi		

Earthquake

♣ Read this telex report of an earthquake in Mexico City in 1985.
♣ List below all the problems caused by such a massive earthquake.

7.20am Thursday 19 September 1985. Third largest earthquake hits Mexico

City. 7,000 people dead. Huge tidal wave (called tsunami) swamped 2 cargo

and 15 fishing boats. Crews missing. In Mexico city hundreds of buildings

collapsed including three main hospitals. Water mains burst, gas mains

broken. Over 100 fires started. Thousands of people homeless, frightened and

without food, water, warm clothing or medicine. Fear of diseases like

typhoid. Nights are freezing cold. Message ends.

Problems caused by an earthquake

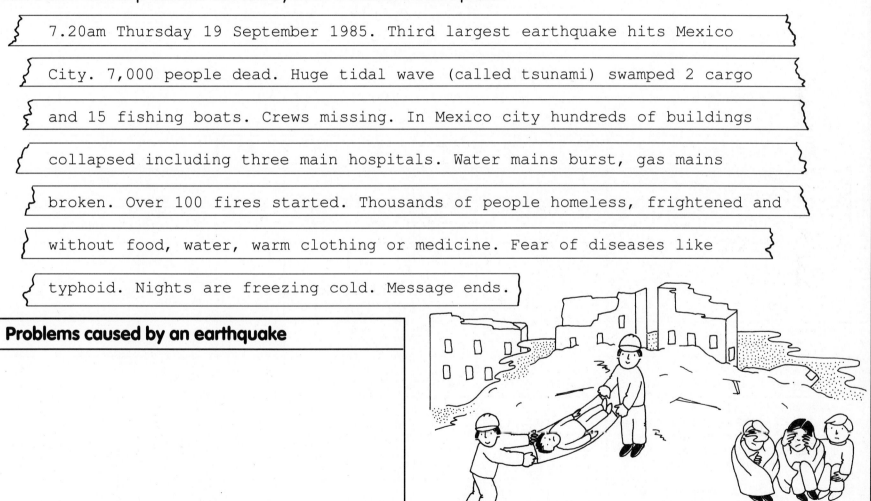

Name _____

Surveying the streets

Surveying the streets

♣ Make a survey of two (or more) streets near school. Use one copy of this sheet for each street.
♣ Fill in the table by putting a cross in the box which best describes what you think about the street (where 1 = poor/the worst and 6 = good/the best).

Town _____   Street name _____

Date _____   Time _____

Street features	1	2	3	4	5	6	
The pavement: full of holes and bumpy							even and flat
Grass verges: none							wide grass verges
Parked cars or lorries: many vehicles							no vehicles
Litter: a lot of litter							no litter
Trees: no trees							many trees
Area to play: no special play area							special play area
Air quality: lots of fumes							no fumes
Buildings: rundown, need repairs							in good condition
Other (add your own feature):							

A change for the better

The two scenes below show the same coal-mining valley in South Wales in 1900 and 1993.
♣ Make a list, on the back of this sheet, of all the changes you can spot between the valley in 1900 and in 1993. After each change, say how the environment has been improved.

1900

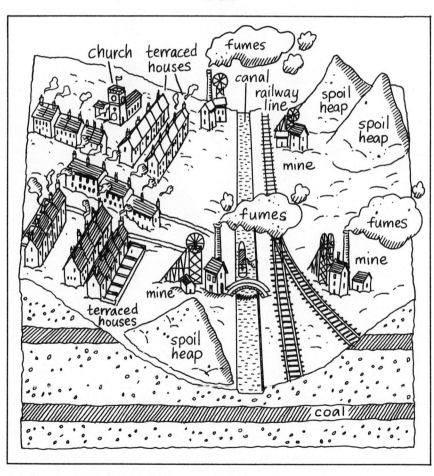

1993

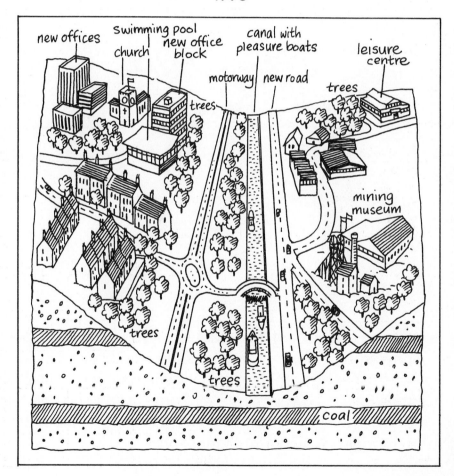

Name _____

Consequences

Consequences

It is proposed to build a dam in the Eton Valley to create a reservoir. Everything west of the dam, up to a height of 110m, would be flooded. Two people have given their opinions on the scheme.

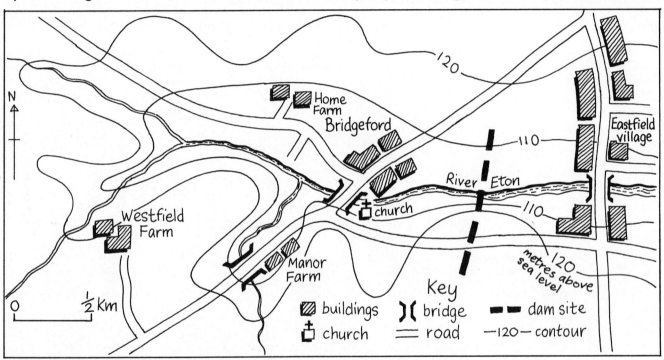

I'm a water sports fan, so I want to see the scheme go ahead.

We have a beautiful old church and the water would ruin it.

✤ Write on the back of this sheet what you think these people would say:
• John Vernon – unemployed building worker living in Eastfield;
• Alice Case – has run the Post Office in Bridgeford for 20 years;
• James Bailey – owner of Barley Construction and Civil Engineering Company;
• Mary Wainwright – has just converted the Old Mill in Bridgeford into a restaurant;
• Tim Manning – owner of Manor Farm;
• Gwen Taylor – owner of Westfield Farm.

Name _____

A village in India

This is a picture of a village in India.
❧ Label the picture using the words in the boxes at the bottom of the page.
❧ Colour the huts in yellow.   ❧ Colour the tracks in brown.   ❧ Colour the trees in green.

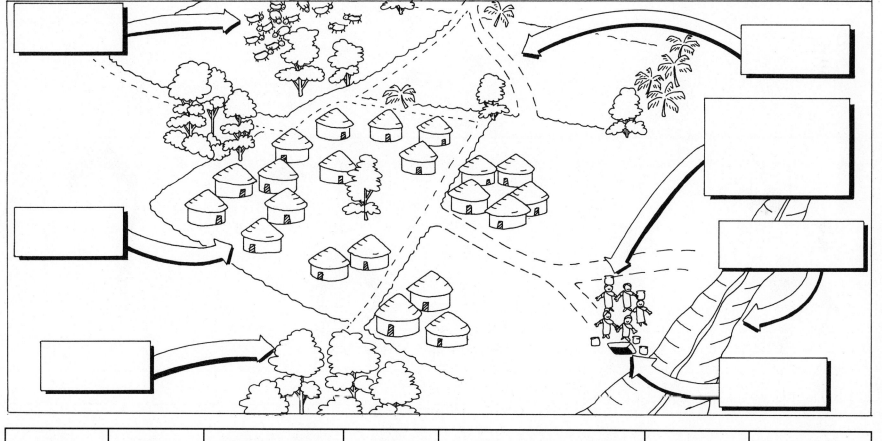

| tree | hut | dried up river | well | women carrying water | track | cattle |

Using water in India

Name _____

Using water in India

This is a pool in the countryside of India.
❧ Colour in blue the things to do with drinking.
❧ Colour in green the things to do with washing.

❧ Why is this water not very safe for people to drink? _____

_____

_____

Name _____

A letter to India

Mary lives in England. She writes letters to her pen-friend, Rashni, who lives in India.
♣ Colour in the pictures, then cut them out and arrange them in the correct order.

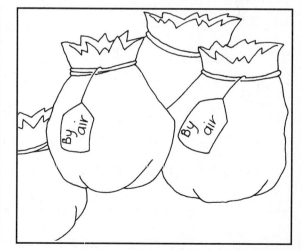

Chanda's day

Chanda's day

Chanda lives in a village in India. The clock diagram shows how she spends her day.
♣ Fill in the chart below to show how much time she spends on each activity.

Name _____

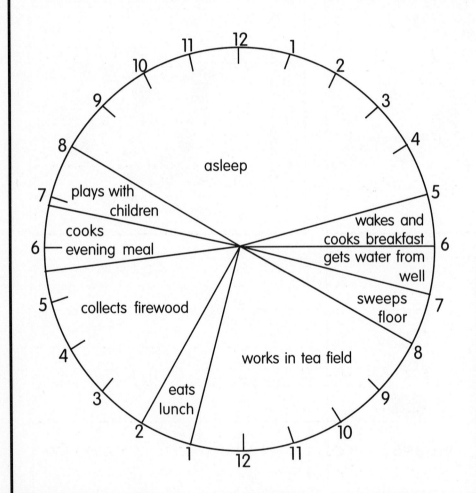

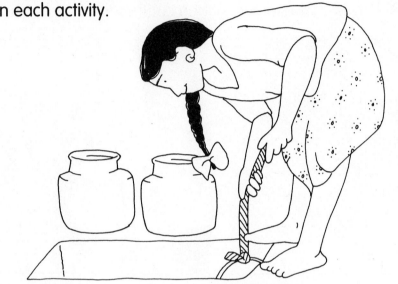

Activity	Amount of time
Sleeping	
At work in the fields	
Collecting wood	
Preparing meals	
Fetching water	

136

Name _____

My day

♣ Fill in the clock diagram below to show how you spend your day.
Shade in different colours the times when you:

- are asleep;
- go to school;
- work at school;

- eat breakfast, lunch, evening meal, supper and other snacks;

- return from school;
- work at home;
- play.

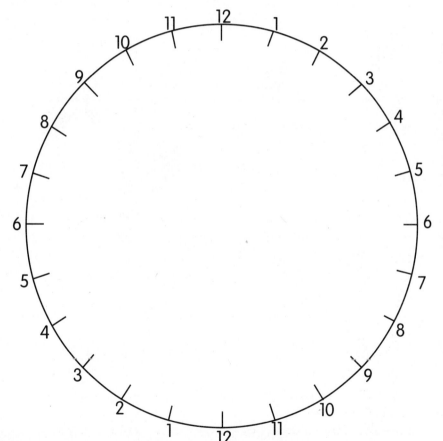

♣ Now complete the chart below:

Activity	Amount of time
Sleeping	
Working at school	
Eating	
Travelling	
Working at home	
Playing	

♣ How is your day different from that of someone who lives in an Indian village?

A meal in India

Name _____

A meal in India

The Rajiv family are sitting down to a meal.
♣ Look at their foods on the cloth.
♣ List each food under the correct heading.

Fruit	Vegetables	Meat	Drink

paratha (fried chapatti)
- a kind of flat bread

keema
(spicy lamb)

vegetable curry
(peas, carrots,
potatoes)

rice (boiled, brown)

coconut barfi (to drink)

pakoras (small pieces
of potatoes + other
vegetables fried in batter)

The weather in Delhi

Name _____

The weather in Delhi

✤ Look at the figures below for rainfall in Delhi.
✤ Use the figures to complete the graph – January has been done for you.

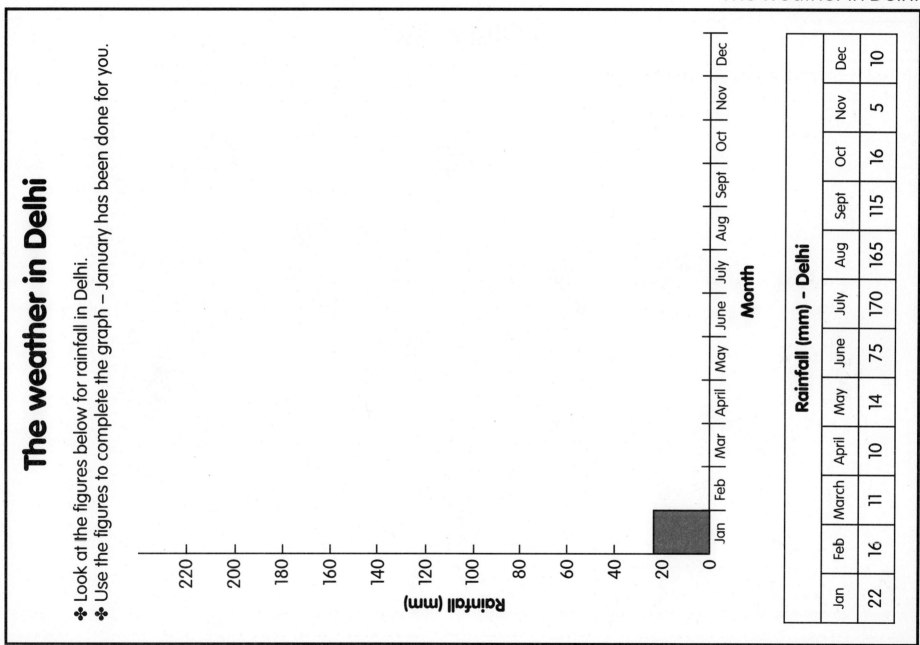

Rainfall (mm) – Delhi

Jan	Feb	March	April	May	June	July	Aug	Sept	Oct	Nov	Dec
22	16	11	10	14	75	170	165	115	16	5	10

Village life

Name _____

Village life

This is what some people think about their village in India.

* ❧ Make a list of the good things about village life.
* ❧ Make a list of the bad things about village life.
* ❧ What are the main problems facing the people who live in the village?

Name _____

The United Kingdom

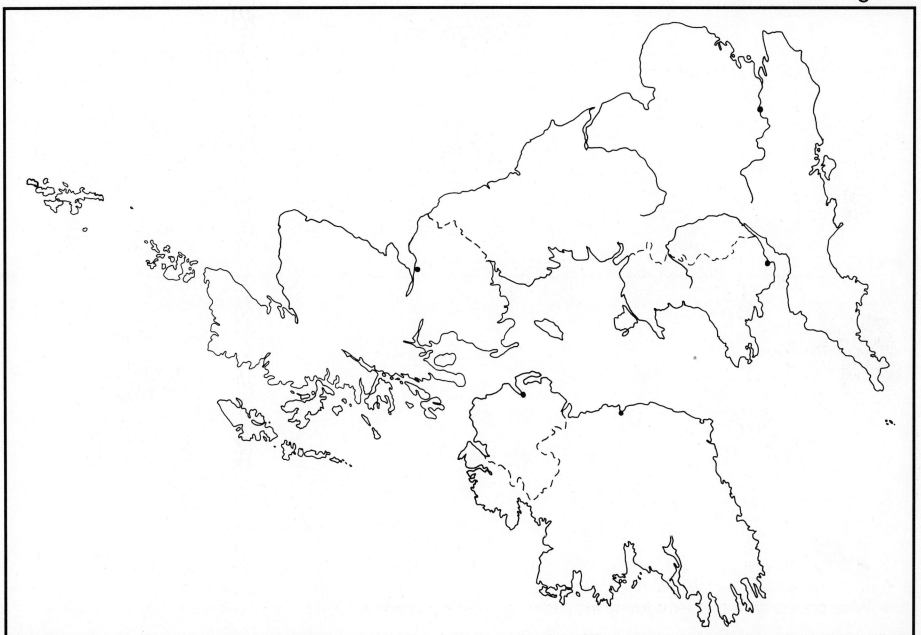

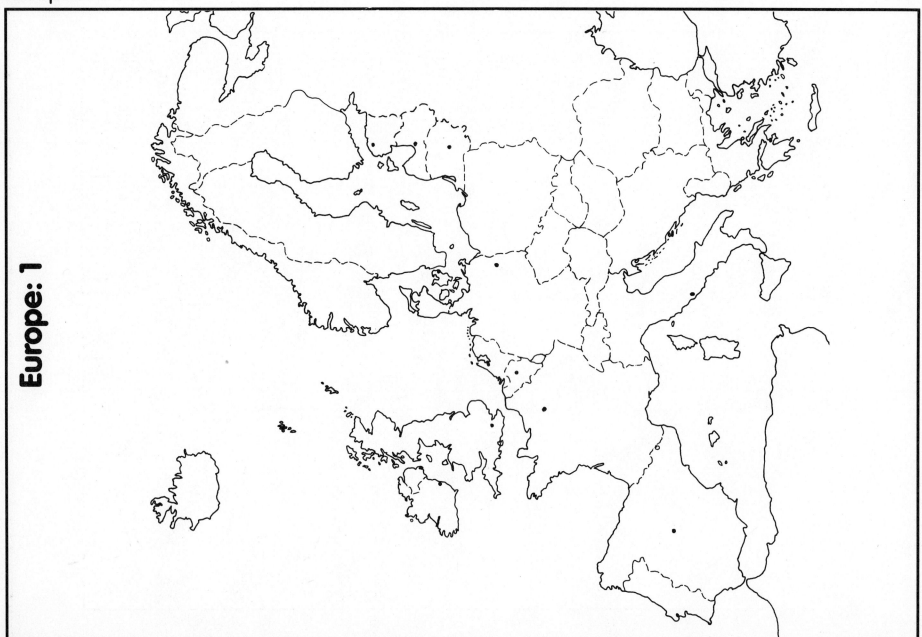

Europe: 1

Name _____

Europe: 2

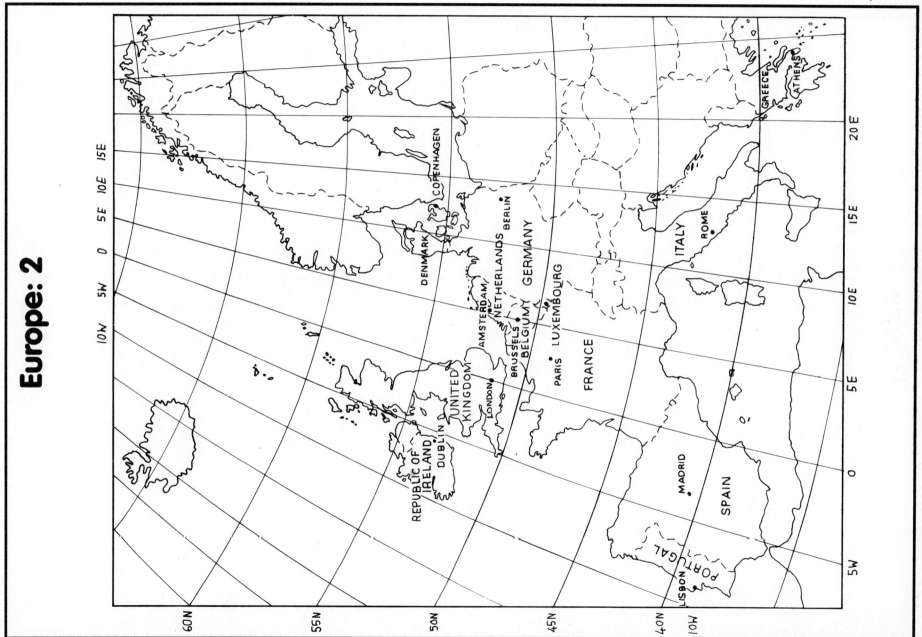

The world

Name _____

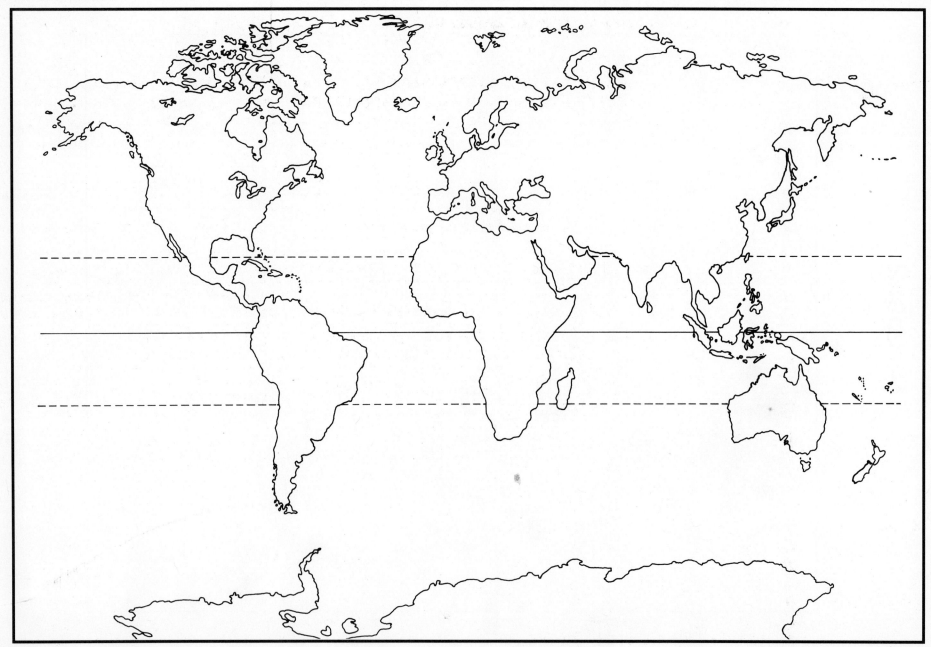